1982

ELEMENTS OF MODERN
ABSTRACT ALGEBRA

HARPER'S MATHEMATICS SERIES

Charles A. Hutchinson, Editor

ELEMENTS OF MODERN
ABSTRACT ALGEBRA

by

KENNETH S. MILLER, Ph.D.

Associate Professor of Mathematics
New York University

HARPER & ROW, PUBLISHERS

New York, Evanston, and London

Library of Congress Catalog Card Number : 58-5101

C O N T E N T S

Chapter 3. Fields

References

Appendix. Sets

Index

PREFACE

In this book we have attempted to present in a simple and concise manner the elementary facts of the mathematical discipline usually given the title modern algebra. We have considered the nucleus of ideas clustered around the concepts of groups, rings, and fields. It is not our intention to be encyclopedic; rather we have laid a broad foundation upon which the student can build further. Toward this goal, our definitions and axioms are the most general; hence it will never be necessary for the student to "relearn" any concept. For example, we prefer to define abstract groups at the outset rather than introduce them via permutation groups, and to define general ideals rather than to use first special ideals in the field of real numbers. The ideas are developed as far as seems practical in a book designed for upperclassmen mathematics majors or beginning graduate students. Zorn's lemma and other results involving "noncountability" axioms are not used in the text proper, although a discussion appears in the Appendix.

The formal prerequisites necessary to an understanding of the text are nil. A knowledge of the real and complex number system and high school algebra, is, with minor exceptions, sufficient. However, that elusive quality called "mathematical maturity" and the ability to reason abstractly are necessary for a complete appreciation of the subject matter.

Mr. C. W. Langley of New York University and Mr. L. E. Blumenson of Columbia University both carefully read the entire manuscript and offered many valuable suggestions for the improvement of the text. In particular Mr. Langley was very helpful in the preparation of the Appendix. I take this opportunity to express my sincere appreciation for their efforts.

October, 1957   K. S. M.

ELEMENTS OF MODERN
ABSTRACT ALGEBRA

CHAPTER I

Groups

1.1 Introduction

We shall be interested in abstract algebra purely as a mathematical discipline. The theorems we shall deduce will be reward enough, and "practical" applications of the fundamental theorems will be of little interest to us. However, the reader should not infer that applications do not exist;† they are simply foreign to our main theme of development.

It would be desirable, at the beginning, to place the theory of groups in its proper perspective with regard to the whole of abstract algebra. However, unless the reader has some preliminary knowledge of groups, rings, integral domains, and fields, nothing would be gained by such an exposition. Once we have analyzed the various topics mentioned above, the rôle of group theory will become crystalline.

Without more apology, we lay down the classical definition of an abstract group.

Definition. A *group* G is a collection of objects for which a binary operation $*$ is defined. This operation is subject to the following laws :

1. *Closure*. If a and b are in G, then $a*b$ is in G.

2. *Associativity*. If a, b, and c are in G, then $(a*b)*c = a*(b*c)$.

3. *Identity*. There exists a unique element e in G (called the identity element) such that for all a in G, $a*e = e*a = a$.

4. *Inverse*. For every a in G there exists a unique element a' in G called the inverse of a, such that $a*a' = a'*a = e$.

---

† Cf., for example, H. Margenau and G. M. Murphy, *The Mathematics of Physics and Chemistry*, D. van Nostrand Co., Inc., 1943; and H. Weyl, *Theory of Groups and Quantum Mechanics*, Dover Publications Inc., 1949.

Before giving concrete examples of groups, let us discuss the axioms themselves in some detail. We say a group is a collection of objects. By this we mean a set of objects having some given property. For example, the property of being an integer, the property of being a cube root of unity, the property of being a real continuous function on the unit interval. For every two objects a and b, a "binary operation" is defined. By a binary operation we mean an operation on two objects, such as multiplication or addition. In these cases we write ab or $a + b$, respectively, instead of $a*b$. In Section 1.4 we shall give examples of groups in which the binary operation is neither addition nor multiplication. The binary operation is frequently called "group multiplication."

The four axioms are generally referred to as the "closure axiom," the "associativity axiom," etc. Axiom 1 states that if the binary operation is applied to any two objects in the group, the resulting object is also in the group. For example, consider the set of all even integers with addition as the binary operation. Clearly the sum of any two even integers is an even integer and we can say that the "even integers are closed with respect to addition." On the other hand, for example, the set of all odd integers is not closed with respect to addition since the sum of two odd integers is not an odd integer. Axiom 2 states that the binary operation is associative. This is often not an easy axiom to verify, although the operations commonly defined on most mathematical objects, for example, numbers, matrices, transformations, are associative. Note that since $(a*b)*c = a*(b*c)$ the symbol $a*b*c$ is unambiguous. Axiom 3 states the existence of an identity element. In the case of real numbers, with multiplication as the binary operation "1" is the identity, since $1 \cdot \alpha = \alpha \cdot 1 = \alpha$ for any real number α. If the binary operation is addition, "0" is the identity, since $\alpha + 0 = 0 + \alpha = \alpha$. Axiom 4 postulates the existence of an inverse. For multiplication the inverse of α ($\alpha \neq 0$) is $1/\alpha$ or α^{-1} since $\alpha \cdot \alpha^{-1} = \alpha^{-1} \cdot \alpha = 1$. For addition, the inverse of α is $-\alpha$ since $\alpha + (-\alpha) = -\alpha + \alpha = 0$.

1.2 Examples of Groups

A. Let us consider the set Z of all real numbers which have the property of being an integer. That is, we shall consider the numbers $\cdots, -3, -2, -1, 0, +1, +2, +3, \cdots$. We shall show that Z is a group with respect to the binary operation of addition. To show that Z is a group we must prove that the four axioms hold for Z.

Suppose n and m are integers. Clearly then $n + m$ is an integer. Hence Axiom 1 is verified. Also Axiom 2 is trivial, since if n, m, and p

are three integers, then $(n + m) + p = n + (m + p)$. The number 0 is in Z and is an identity, since $0 + n = n + 0 = n$ for any n in Z. Clearly it is the only number in Z with this property. Finally if n is an integer, $- n$ is also an integer and $n + (- n) = - n + n = 0$. It is clear that the inverse $- n$ of n is unique. Hence Axioms 1–4 have been verified and the set of integers forms a group under addition.

We sometimes say G is an _additive group_ to indicate that the binary operation is addition. Similarly we would say _multiplicative group_ if the binary operation were multiplication. As a simplification in nota-tion we shall write $m + (- n)$ simply as $m - n$ when the binary operation is addition.

B. As a second example, let us consider the four fourth roots of unity, namely $+ 1, - 1, + i, -i$, where $i = \sqrt{- 1}$. We shall show that these numbers form a multiplicative group M. Note that our first example, Z, had an infinite number of elements, while our second example, M, has a finite number of elements. Groups with only a finite number of elements are appropriately called "finite groups." Our original axioms make no restrictions as to the number of elements in a group (other than that there be at least one—the identity).

Let us verify Axiom 1 for M :

Define operation

$$1 \cdot 1 = 1$$
$$1 \cdot (- 1) = - 1$$
$$1 \cdot i = i$$
$$1 \cdot (- i) = - i$$
$$(-1) \cdot 1 = - 1$$
$$(- 1) \cdot (- 1) = 1$$
$$(- 1) \cdot i = - i$$
$$(- 1) \cdot (- i) = i$$
$$i \cdot 1 = i \tag{1.1}$$
$$i \cdot (- 1) = - i$$
$$i \cdot i = - 1$$
$$i \cdot (- i) = 1$$
$$(- i) \cdot 1 = - i$$
$$(- i) \cdot (- 1) = i$$
$$(- i) \cdot i = 1$$
$$(- i) \cdot (- i) = - 1.$$

Note that in a finite group we can exhibit all possible multiplications.

It is often convenient to arrange them in a table (called a multiplication table) as indicated below.

	$+1$	-1	$+i$	$-i$
$+1$	$+1$	-1	$+i$	$-i$
-1	-1	$+1$	$-i$	$+i$
$+i$	$+i$	$-i$	-1	$+1$
$-i$	$-i$	$+i$	$+1$	-1

Clearly every element on the right-hand side of Equations 1.1, (or entry in the table) is $+1$, -1, $+i$, or $-i$. Hence M is "closed." As before, Axiom 2 is trivial. The identity is clearly $+1$ and the inverses of 1, -1, i, $-i$ are 1, -1, $-i$, and i, respectively. Thus M is a finite multiplicative group.

The number of elements in a finite group is called the *order* of the group. For example, M is of order four.

1.3 The Left and Right Axioms

In dealing with abstract groups it is convenient to write ab instead of using the special symbol $*$ and writing $a*b$. The quantity ab is to be interpreted as $a + b$ or $a \cdot b$, etc., as the particular case in question may demand. Similarly, we write a^{-1} to indicate the inverse a' of a, where if we have an additive group, a^{-1} is to be interpreted as "$-a$." Also we use such notation as a^n to mean $a*a* \cdots *a$ (n factors) and a^{-m} as shorthand for $a^{-1}*a^{-1}* \cdots *a^{-1}$ (m factors).

We have given the classical axioms in Section 1.1. Here we shall give the "left axioms" and the "right axioms." They appear weaker than the classical axioms, but we shall show them to be fully equivalent to these.

Left Axioms:
1. Same as classical axiom 1.
2. Same as classical axiom 2.
3. There exists at least one element e in G such that for all a in G, $ea = a$.
4. For some e of Axiom 3 and for every a in G there exists at least one element a^{-1} in G such that $a^{-1}a = e$.

Note that the classical axioms have been weakened so that the identity is assumed to be a *left* identity only and furthermore is not assumed to be unique. Similar remarks apply to the inverse. Clearly if a set G satisfies the classical axioms, it satisfies the left axioms. We shall show that the converse is true.

First we show that a^{-1} is a right inverse as well as a left inverse. Consider $(a^{-1}a)a^{-1}$. Now

$$(a^{-1}a)a^{-1} = ea^{-1} = a^{-1} \tag{1.2}$$

by Axioms 4 and 3, respectively. Furthermore,

$$(a^{-1})^{-1}[(a^{-1}a)a^{-1}] = (a^{-1})^{-1}a^{-1} = e \tag{1.3}$$

by Equation 1.2 and Axiom 4. Also, applying Axiom 2 to the above expression,

$$[(a^{-1})^{-1}a^{-1}][aa^{-1}] = e(aa^{-1}) = aa^{-1} \tag{1.4}$$

by Axioms 4 and 3, respectively. From Equations 1.3 and 1.4 we conclude

$$aa^{-1} = e \tag{1.5}$$

and hence a^{-1} is a *right* as well as a left inverse. To prove that e is also a right identity, we have

$$ae = a(a^{-1}a) = (aa^{-1})a = ea = a$$

by Axioms 4, 2, Equation 1.5, and Axiom 3, respectively.

The fact that e is unique is shown by

$$e' = ee' = e'e = e,$$

where e' is any other identity. For $e' = ee'$, since e is an identity, and $ee' = e'e$, since e' is both a left and a right identity.

To show that a^{-1} is unique, suppose b is any element in G such that $ba = e$. Then

$$b = be = b(aa^{-1}) = (ba)a^{-1} = ea^{-1} = a^{-1}.$$

Hence we see that the left axioms are equivalent to the classical axioms. The value of having such a set of axioms, is that given an arbitrary set S, it is easier to prove that an element is *an* inverse rather than *the* inverse, and further to prove that it is only a *left* inverse rather than a left *and* a right inverse. Similar remarks hold for the identity element.

Right Axioms:

1. Same as classical axiom 1.
2. Same as classical axiom 2.

3. There exists at least one element e in G such that for all a in G, $ae = a$.

4. For every e of Axiom 3 and for every a in G there exists at least one element a^{-1} in G such that $aa^{-1} = e$.

As above, we may prove that the right axioms imply the classical axioms. However, if we postulate, say a *left* identity and a *right* inverse, the set is not necessarily a group, as can be shown by examples.

From the above discussion we can prove the following simple theorems.

Theorem 1. The inverse of a^{-1} is a.

Proof: $(a^{-1})^{-1}a^{-1} = e$ by definition. Multiply both sides of the equation on the right by a; then

$$[(a^{-1})^{-1}a^{-1}]a = (a^{-1})^{-1}(a^{-1}a) = (a^{-1})^{-1}e = (a^{-1})^{-1}$$

and $ea = a$. Hence

$$(a^{-1})^{-1} = a.$$

Another trivial, but useful theorem concerning inverses, is the following.

Theorem 2. The inverse of ab is $b^{-1}a^{-1}$.

Proof: $(ab)(b^{-1}a^{-1}) = a(bb^{-1})a^{-1} = aea^{-1} = aa^{-1} = e$.

This can, of course, be generalized to any finite number of factors. That is,

$$(a_1a_2 \cdots a_{n-1}a_n)^{-1} = a_n^{-1}a_{n-1}^{-1} \cdots a_2^{-1}a_1^{-1}.$$

1.4 Further Examples

A. The two examples previously given have been examples of *commutative* groups. That is, $ab = ba$ for all a, b in G. Groups in which this is true are called *abelian* or commutative groups. Additive abelian groups are frequently called *modules*. We shall now consider an example of a noncommutative group in which the group operation is neither addition nor multiplication but "composition."

Consider, then, the set of all possible permutations of the numbers 1, 2, 3. We may write them as

$$I = \begin{pmatrix} 1 & 2 & 3 \\ 1 & 2 & 3 \end{pmatrix} \qquad T_1 = \begin{pmatrix} 1 & 2 & 3 \\ 1 & 3 & 2 \end{pmatrix} \qquad T_2 = \begin{pmatrix} 1 & 2 & 3 \\ 2 & 1 & 3 \end{pmatrix}$$

$$T_3 = \begin{pmatrix} 1 & 2 & 3 \\ 2 & 3 & 1 \end{pmatrix} \qquad T_4 = \begin{pmatrix} 1 & 2 & 3 \\ 3 & 1 & 2 \end{pmatrix} \qquad T_5 = \begin{pmatrix} 1 & 2 & 3 \\ 3 & 2 & 1 \end{pmatrix}.$$

The permutations I, T_1, T_2, T_3, T_4, T_5 will be the elements of our set G.

We say, for example, T_1 is the permutation which takes 1 into 1, 2 into 3, and 3 into 2. We could also write T_1 as $\begin{pmatrix} 2 & 1 & 3 \\ 3 & 1 & 2 \end{pmatrix}$ or $\begin{pmatrix} 2 & 3 & 1 \\ 3 & 2 & 1 \end{pmatrix}$ since these permutations also take 1 into 1, 2 into 3, and 3 into 2. That is, the permutation is unchanged by switching around the elements in the first row if the corresponding elements in the second row are also switched in the same manner. The group operation (called composition or substitution) is defined as follows. If T is a permutation which takes α into β and S is a permutation which takes β into γ, then ST is that permutation which takes α into γ. For example,

$$T_1 T_2 = \begin{pmatrix} 1 & 2 & 3 \\ 1 & 3 & 2 \end{pmatrix} \begin{pmatrix} 1 & 2 & 3 \\ 2 & 1 & 3 \end{pmatrix} = \begin{pmatrix} 1 & 2 & 3 \\ 3 & 1 & 2 \end{pmatrix} = T_4.$$

For the permutations I, T_1, T_2, T_3, T_4, T_5 we can construct a multiplication table as in Section 1.2.

	I	T_1	T_2	T_3	T_4	T_5
I	I	T_1	T_2	T_3	T_4	T_5
T_1	T_1	I	T_4	T_5	T_2	T_3
T_2	T_2	T_3	I	T_1	T_5	T_4
T_3	T_3	T_2	T_5	T_4	I	T_1
T_4	T_4	T_5	T_1	I	T_3	T_2
T_5	T_5	T_4	T_3	T_2	T_1	I

It is easily seen that G is a noncommutative group whose identity element is I and where I, T_1, T_2, T_4, T_3, T_5 are the inverses of I, T_1, T_2, T_3, T_4, and T_5, respectively.

This group can be generalized. Consider the totality of transformations

$$T = \begin{pmatrix} 1 & 2 & 3 & \cdots & n \\ i_1 & i_2 & i_3 & \cdots & i_n \end{pmatrix} \tag{1.6}$$

which permute the n integers $1, 2, \cdots, n$. This set of transformations will be shown to form a group, $\mathfrak{S}_n$, called the *symmetric group*. (We use the first n integers; clearly any n distinct objects could be used.) Since the number of permutations of n objects is $n!$, there are $n!$ transformations in $\mathfrak{S}_n$; hence $\mathfrak{S}_n$ will be a group of order $n!$.

Our definition of group multiplication is the same as in the previous example.   Clearly TS where T and S are permutations is a permutation of the n integers.   Hence $\mathfrak{S}_n$ is closed.   The associativity will be left as an exercise for the reader.   The identity is

$$I = \begin{pmatrix} 1 & 2 & 3 \cdots n \\ 1 & 2 & 3 \cdots n \end{pmatrix}$$

and the inverse of T (Equation 1.6) is

$$T^{-1} = \begin{pmatrix} i_1 & i_2 \cdots i_n \\ 1 & 2 \cdots n \end{pmatrix}.$$

We shall return to this example later.

B. As another example of a group whose elements are not numbers, consider the set of all rotations of points in 3-space about a fixed point. If a rotation A is followed by a rotation B it is equivalent to a single rotation C, which we shall write $C = BA$.   The inverse of a rotation A is that rotation A^{-1} which carries each point back to its original position. The identity rotation is that rotation which leaves every point invariant.

C. If a and b are two integers, we may always write

$$a + b = 7q + c \tag{1.7}$$

where q and c are integers and

$$0 \leqq c \leqq 6.$$

For example,

$$12 + 8 = 2(7) + 6$$

and

$$-19 + 3 = -3(7) + 5.$$

Let us now define a new type of addition called "addition modulo 7," and written $a +_7 b$.   By this we mean

$$a +_7 b = c,$$

that is, we add a and b and then cast out multiples of 7.   For example,

$$12 +_7 8 = 6.$$

So from this point of view, any two integers whose difference is divisible by 7 will be considered identical.   [Another way of writing this is to say

$$20 \equiv 6 \quad (\bmod\ 7)$$

which is read "20 is congruent to 6 modulo 7," and simply means that 7 divides $20 - 6$.   This is standard notation in the theory of numbers.] Now consider the integers

$$\{0,\ 1,\ 2,\ 3,\ 4,\ 5,\ 6\}.$$

We shall show that they form a group under the binary operation of "addition modulo 7." (For convenience we drop the subscript "7" on the plus sign.)

First, the set is closed, for

$$
\begin{array}{llll}
0+0=0 & 1+1=2 & 2+2=4 & 3+3=6 \\
0+1=1 & 1+2=3 & 2+3=5 & 3+4=0 \\
0+2=2 & 1+3=4 & 2+4=6 & 3+5=1 \\
0+3=3 & 1+4=5. & 2+5=0 & 3+6=2 \\
0+4=4 & 1+5=6 & 2+6=1 & \\
0+5=5 & 1+6=0 & & \\
0+6=6 & & &
\end{array}
$$

$$
\begin{array}{lll}
4+4=1 & 5+5=3 & 6+6=5 \\
4+5=2 & 5+6=4 & \\
4+6=3 & &
\end{array}
$$

Associativity is clear, the identity is 0, and the inverses of 0, 1, 2, 3, 4, 5, 6 are 0, 6, 5, 4, 3, 2, and 1, respectively.

This example and its generalizations will be used later in our work on finite fields (cf. Chapter 3).

1.5 Subgroups

Definition. A collection of elements H in G is said to form a _subgroup_ of G if H forms a group relative to the binary operation defined in G.

For example, the totality of even integers forms a subgroup of the totality of integers with respect to addition. If G is a group, then clearly G itself is a subgroup of G. Also the group consisting of the identity e alone is a subgroup of G. This group is frequently denoted by I. The subgroups G and I are called _improper_ subgroups of G. Any other subgroup of G is called a _proper_ subgroup of G.

The totality of real numbers E forms a group under addition, while the totality of rational numbers unequal to zero forms a group S under multiplication. Even though S is a subset of E it is not a subgroup of E because different binary operations are postulated in E and S.

A theorem which establishes a convenient criterion for determining whether a given subset H of a group G is a subgroup, is the following.

Theorem 3. A set H in G is a subgroup of G if and only if when a, b are in H, then ab^{-1} is also in H.

Proof: Suppose H is a subgroup and a and b are in H. If b is in H, then by the "inverse axiom," b^{-1} is in H, and by the closure axiom

Given: $a, b \in H$, $ab^{-1} \in H$. + H is subset of G
Prove: H subgroup of G

ab^{-1} is in H. On the other hand, suppose a and b are in H and ab^{-1} is in H. Since a is in H, $aa^{-1} = e$ is in H. Similarly, $eb^{-1} = b^{-1}$ is in H. Furthermore $a(b^{-1})^{-1} = ab$ is in H, and H is a subgroup.

In the previous section we considered a group $\mathfrak{S}_n$ called the _symmetric group_. An important subgroup of $\mathfrak{S}_n$ is the _alternating group_ $\mathfrak{A}_n$ which we shall now define. Consider the n variables $x_1, x_2, \cdots, x_n$ and the product of their differences:

$$X = \prod_{\substack{i=1 \\ j=1 \\ i>j}}^{n} (x_i - x_j).$$

If the variables $x_1, x_2, \cdots, x_n$ are permuted, that is, if x_1 is replaced by x_{k_1}, x_2 by x_{k_2}, etc., where $k_1, k_2, \cdots, k_n$ is a rearrangement of the integers $1, 2, \cdots, n$, then X will change sign or not change sign depending on whether an odd or an even number of the terms $(x_i - x_j)$ are interchanged. For example, for $n = 4$,

$$X = (x_4 - x_1)(x_4 - x_2)(x_4 - x_3)(x_3 - x_2)(x_3 - x_1)(x_2 - x_1).$$

Now if the numbers 1, 2, 3, 4 are permuted to, say 2, 1, 3, 4, the above expression becomes

$$(x_4 - x_2)(x_4 - x_1)(x_4 - x_3)(x_3 - x_1)(x_3 - x_2)(x_1 - x_2)$$

which is precisely $- X$.

Now consider T, an element of $\mathfrak{S}_n$, as operating on X, $T(X)$. The result will be either $+ X$ or $- X$:

$$T(X) = \pm X.$$

We shall call a transformation T of $\mathfrak{S}_n$ an _even permutation_ if

$$T(X) = + X$$

and we shall call T an _odd permutation_ if

$$T(X) = - X.$$

Clearly every element of $\mathfrak{S}_n$ is either an even permutation or an odd permutation. The totality of even permutations will be called the _alternating group_ $\mathfrak{A}_n$ of $\mathfrak{S}_n$. We leave it to the reader to verify that $\mathfrak{A}_n$ _is_ a group.

The composition of two even permutations is even, the composition of two odd permutations is even, and the composition of an odd permutation and an even permutation is odd. For, let S_1 and S_2 be even permutations and T_1 and T_2 be odd permutations. Then

$$S_1 S_2(X) = S_1[S_2(X)] = S_1(X) = X,$$
$$T_1 T_2(X) = T_1[T_2(X)] = T_1(-X) = -(-X) = X,$$
$$T_1 S_1(X) = T_1[S_1(X)] = T_1(X) = -X,$$
$$S_1 T_1(X) = S_1[T_1(X)] = S_1(-X) = -X.$$

The order of $\mathfrak{S}_n$ was seen to be $n!$. We assert that the order of $\mathfrak{A}_n$ is $n!/2$. To prove this assertion, suppose that there are μ distinct even permutations

$$S_1, S_2, \cdots, S_\mu$$

and ν distinct odd permutations

$$T_1, T_2, \cdots, T_\nu.$$

We shall show that $\mu = \nu$ and hence that the order of $\mathfrak{A}_n$ is $n!/2$. For consider

$$T_1 T_1, T_1 T_2, T_1 T_3, \cdots, T_1 T_\nu.$$

By the above remarks, $T_1 T_i$ is even. The permutations $T_1 T_j$ are also distinct. For suppose that

$$T_1 T_j = T_1 T_k.$$

Then multiplying by T_1^{-1} on the left (operations carried out in $\mathfrak{S}_n$, and hence T_1^{-1} exists) we obtain

$$T_j = T_k$$

which implies that $j = k$ since the T_i were assumed distinct. Hence $\mu \geq \nu$. Similarly,

$$T_1 S_1, T_1 S_2, \cdots, T_1 S_\mu$$

are all odd, and from $T_1 S_j = T_1 S_k$ follows $S_j = S_k$ or $j = k$. Hence the permutations are all distinct and $\nu \geq \mu$. From the two inequalities $\mu \geq \nu$, $\nu \geq \mu$ we conclude

$$\mu = \nu = \frac{n!}{2}.$$

We shall now consider the concept of a *cyclic* group. Suppose G is a group and a is an element in G. Then the set of elements a^n, $n = 0$, $\pm 1, \pm 2, \cdots$ forms a group H called the *cyclic subgroup generated by a*. This statement is easy to prove. For

$$a^n a^m = a^{n+m}$$

is an element in H. (Recall the definition of a^n, Section 1.3.) The inverse of a^n is a^{-n}, the identity is $a^0 = e$. If G is finite, not all the a^n are distinct. Clearly H is an abelian group. Hence a noncommutative group may have commutative subgroups.

If every element of a group G can be written as a^n, where a is an element in G and n is an integer, then we say that G is a *cyclic group*. For example, the group M of the four fourth roots of unity forms a cyclic group with generator i, since

$$i = i$$
$$(i)^2 = -1$$
$$(i)^3 = -i$$
$$i^0 = (i)^4 = 1.$$

The reader may verify that $-i$ could also be used as a generator for M, whereas 1 or -1 could not.

Suppose now that G is an arbitrary finite group of order greater than one. Let a be an arbitrary element in G unequal to the identity element. Consider the elements

$$e = a^0, a^1, a^2, \cdots .$$

Clearly a^n is in G since G is a group. Now since G contains at most a finite number of elements, not all the a^k are distinct. Hence some $a^s = a^t$ with, say, $t > s$. Then $a^{t-s} = e$. That is, some $a^k = e$ with $k > 0$. Let m be the smallest positive integer with the property that $a^m = e$. We shall show that the m elements

$$e = a^0, a^1, a^2, \cdots , a^{m-1}$$

form a subgroup H of order m. For

$$a^r a^t = a^{r+t}$$

and $r + t$ is an integer which may be written as

$$r + t = qm + u,$$

where $0 \leq u < m$ and q is an integer. Hence

$$a^{r+t} = a^{qm+u} = a^{qm}a^u = (a^m)^q a^u = e^q a^u = a^u$$

and a^u is in H. The identity in H is $e = a^0$ and the inverse of a^r ($r \neq 0$) is a^{m-r}. It remains but to show that $e, a, a^2, \cdots , a^{m-1}$ are all distinct. Suppose $a^j = a^k$ with $m > j > k > 0$. Then it follows that $a^{j-k} = e$. Therefore $j - k$ is zero or a multiple of m. Neither possibility is tenable.

1.6 Cosets

Definition. If G is a group, H a subgroup of G, and a any element in G, then the set of elements ha, h arbitrary in H, is called the *right coset* generated by a and H. It is denoted by Ha. Similarly aH is called the *left coset*.

If G is a group, H a subgroup of G, then clearly every element of G belongs to some coset Ha. An interesting theorem with applications in abstract group theory is the following.

Theorem 4. If two right cosets Ha and Hb have *one* element in common they are identical.

Before proving this theorem we make two definitions. Two sets A and B are said to be equal, written $A = B$, if both sets contain the same elements. Also, by AB is meant the totality of elements of the form $a*b$ where a is in A, b is in B, and $*$ is the binary operation defined among the elements of A and B.

Proof of Theorem 4: Suppose Ha and Hb possess the element c in common. Then c may be written as $c = ha$, and also as $c = h'b$, where h and h' are in H. Hence

$$ha = h'b \qquad \text{and} \qquad a = h^{-1}h'b$$

on multiplying both sides of the last equation on the left by h^{-1}. Since H is a group, $h^{-1}h' = h''$ is an element in H and $a = h''b$. Therefore

$$Ha = H(h''b) = (Hh'')b = Hb.$$

[Since h'' is an element in H, $Hh'' = H$. For if d is in Hh'', $d = hh''$. Clearly hh'' is in H. Conversely, if d is in H, $d = dh''^{-1}h''$ is in Hh'', since dh''^{-1} is in H.] Hence we see that distinct cosets do not overlap. Of course our demonstration (and all future ones involving right cosets) could also have been carried out using left cosets.

Suppose G is a group, H a subgroup, and Ha a right coset. The element "a" that appears on the right of Ha is not unique. If b is any other element in Ha, we may write, by virtue of the previous theorem,

$$Ha = Hb.$$

In particular, if h is in H, then $Hh = H$.

Suppose G is a group and H a subgroup. Then G may be decomposed according to cosets of H, namely,

$$G = H + Ha + Hb + \cdots,$$

where $a, b, \cdots$ are elements in G so chosen that all cosets are distinct. In the above expression the "plus signs" are to be interpreted as: G is the collection of all elements belonging to H plus all the elements belonging to Ha plus all the elements belonging to Hb plus $\cdots$.

The above remark on the decomposition of a group into cosets leads to the following theorem.

Theorem 5. If G is a finite group of order n and H is a subgroup of order r, then r divides n.

Proof: Decompose G according to cosets of H in G,

$$G = H + Ha + Hb + \cdots + Hk.$$

Each coset contains r distinct elements. For let $e = h_1, h_2, \cdots, h_r$ be the elements in H. Then the elements of Ha are

$$h_1a, h_2a, \cdots, h_ra.$$

Suppose

$$h_ia = h_ja;$$

then

$$h_iaa^{-1} = h_jaa^{-1}$$

and

$$h_i = h_j.$$

Hence our assertion that each coset contains r distinct elements is verified. Therefore r divides n, say $n = rs$. The integer s is called the *index* of H in G.

As an immediate corollary of the above theorem, we note that any finite group of prime order has no proper subgroups. Other immediate corollaries are:

Corollary. If G is finite of order n, then the order of the cyclic group generated by any element a in G divides n.

Corollary. A finite group of prime order is cyclic.

Proof: Let G be a group of order p, where p is a prime number. Let a be any element in G unequal to the identity. Then $e, a, a^2, \cdots$ is a subgroup (by a previous corollary) say of order m. Since m divides p by Theorem 5 and $m \neq 1$ since $a \neq e$, we must have $m = p$.

We shall now consider a certain group of translations G and give a graphic example of the group, a subgroup and a coset. Consider the set G of all translations of a fixed point (x_0, y_0) in the plane. (Cf. Figure 1.) That is, a, an element of G, takes the point (x_0, y_0) into the point (x', y') by the translation

$$a: \quad \begin{array}{l} x' = x_0 + \alpha' \\ y' = y_0 + \alpha'', \end{array}$$

where α' and α'' are real numbers. Now let b be a translation which takes (x_0, y_0) into (x'', y''):

$$b: \quad \begin{array}{l} x'' = x_0 + \beta' \\ y'' = y_0 + \beta''. \end{array}$$

We define composition of translations $a*b$ by the formula

$$a*b: \quad \begin{aligned} x &= x_0 + (\alpha' + \beta') \\ y &= y_0 + (\alpha'' + \beta''). \end{aligned}$$

Hence G is a set in which a binary operation has been defined. It will now be shown that G is a group. (We note in passing that since $\alpha' + \beta' = \beta' + \alpha'$, the operation $*$ is commutative, that is, $a*b = b*a$.)

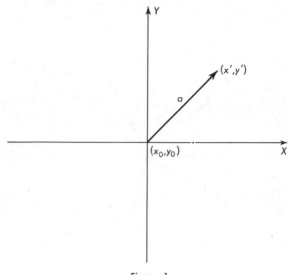

Figure 1

_____ real # + real # = real #

Clearly $a*b$ is a translation and hence G is closed. G is associative since if

$$c: \quad \begin{aligned} \bar{x} &= x_0 + \gamma' \\ \bar{y} &= y_0 + \gamma'', \end{aligned}$$

then

$$(a*b)*c: \quad \begin{aligned} x &= x_0 + (\alpha' + \beta') + \gamma' = x_0 + \alpha' + (\beta' + \gamma') \\ y &= y_0 + (\alpha'' + \beta'') + \gamma'' = y_0 + \alpha'' + (\beta'' + \gamma''), \end{aligned}$$

and by definition

$$a*(b*c): \quad \begin{aligned} x &= x_0 + \alpha' + (\beta' + \gamma') \\ y &= y_0 + \alpha'' + (\beta'' + \gamma''). \end{aligned}$$

The identity translation i is

$$i: \quad \begin{aligned} x &= x_0 \\ y &= y_0 \end{aligned} \qquad \text{since } 0 \text{ is any real \#}$$

and the inverse a^{-1} of a is

$$a^{-1}: \quad \begin{aligned} x &= x_0 - \alpha' \\ y &= y_0 - \alpha''. \end{aligned}$$

*[handwritten: $a * a^{-1} = i$
$x = x_0 + (\alpha' + (-\alpha')) = x$
$y = y_0 + (\beta' + (-\beta')) = y$]*

Hence G is a group.

Now consider the set H of all translations parallel to the x axis, that is, all translations of the form

$$\begin{vmatrix} x = x_0 + \alpha \\ y = y_0. \end{vmatrix}$$

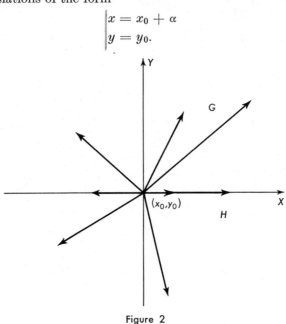

Figure 2

This set is a subgroup, for example, to prove closure:

[handwritten: $\bar{a} \in H$]

$$\bar{a}: \quad \begin{aligned} x &= x_0 + \alpha \\ y &= y_0, \end{aligned}$$

$$\bar{b}: \quad \begin{aligned} x &= x_0 + \beta \\ y &= y_0, \end{aligned}$$

and

$$\bar{a}*\bar{b}: \quad \begin{aligned} x &= x_0 + (\alpha + \beta) \\ y &= y_0. \end{aligned}$$

The group G can be represented graphically as a set of vectors emanating from (x_0, y_0) and H as a set of vectors along the x-axis. (Cf. Figure 2.) Now let

$$d: \quad \begin{aligned} x &= x_0 + \delta' \\ y &= y_0 + \delta'' \end{aligned}$$

be a *fixed* element in G. That is, δ' and δ'' are real numbers which will

*[handwritten bottom: $1^2 - 1^4 b \cdot b''$
so $\bar{a} * \bar{b}^{-1} \in H$?
$\bar{a} * \bar{b}^{-1}: x = x_0 + (\alpha' + (-\beta'))$
$\quad y = y_0$
$\bar{b}^{-1}: x = x_0 - \beta'$
$\quad y = y_0$.
subgroup]*

be fixed for the remainder of this discussion.   The coset Hd consists of
all transformations of the form $\bar{a}*d$, where $\bar{a}$ is in H.   Hence if $\bar{a}$ and d
are as above,

$$\bar{a}*d: \qquad \begin{aligned} x &= x_0 + (\alpha + \delta') \\ y &= y_0 + \delta'' \end{aligned}$$

and all vectors representing elements in Hd can be represented (cf.

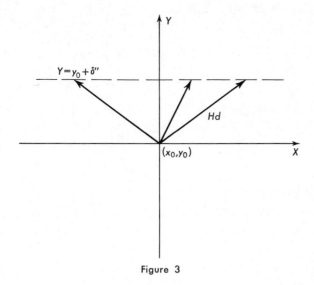

Figure 3

Figure 3) as vectors emanating from (x_0, y_0) and terminating on the
horizontal line whose equation is $Y = y_0 + \delta''$.

1.7 Normal Subgroups

   Theorem 6.   If H is a subgroup of G and a is an element in G, then
the set $K = a^{-1}Ha$ is a subgroup of G.

   Proof: By Theorem 3, all we need show is that $(a^{-1}h'a)(a^{-1}h''a)^{-1}$
is in K, where h' and h'' are arbitrary elements of H.   Now

$$(a^{-1}h'a)(a^{-1}h''a)^{-1} = (a^{-1}h'a)(a^{-1}h''^{-1}a) = (a^{-1}h')(aa^{-1})(h''^{-1}a)$$

$$= (a^{-1}h')e(h''^{-1}a) = a^{-1}h'h''^{-1}a = a^{-1}ha$$

where $h'h''^{-1} = h$ is an element in H since H is a group.   Clearly $a^{-1}ha$
is in K.

   If $a, b, \cdots$ are elements in G, then the subgroups H, $a^{-1}Ha$,
$b^{-1}Hb, \cdots$ of G are called *conjugate subgroups*.

   An important type of subgroup which plays a prominent rôle in all our future investigations of group theory is the *normal* subgroup which we now define.

Definition.   A subgroup H of a group G is called a *normal subgroup* (also a *self-conjugate subgroup*, *invariant subgroup*, *normal divisor*, *distinguished subgroup*) if for all a in G, $a^{-1}Ha = H$.   or contained in

The whole group G and the identity subgroup I form improper normal subgroups of G. A group is said to be *simple* if the only normal subgroups of G are itself and the identity subgroup. Note that every subgroup of a commutative group is normal.

An elementary theorem on normal subgroups is:

Theorem 7.   Let G be a finite group and H a subgroup of index two. Then H is a normal subgroup of G.

Proof: Decompose G according to right cosets of H:

$$G = H + Ha,$$

and according to left cosets:

$$G = H + aH.$$

From these two equations we conclude

$$Ha = aH, \quad \text{or} \quad H = a^{-1}Ha.$$

The above decompositions assume a in G but not in H. Clearly, if a is in H, we certainly have $H = a^{-1}Ha$.

Suppose that H is a subgroup of a group G with the property that the collection of elements $a^{-1}Ha$ is contained in H for every a in G. That is, $a^{-1}ha$ is an element of H for all h in H. But there may be elements of H which cannot be written in this form. We assert that this cannot be. For suppose k is such an element. Now aka^{-1} is an element in H, say h'. Thus

$$aka^{-1} = h', \quad \text{or} \quad k = a^{-1}h'a,$$

which is a contradiction. The definition $H = a^{-1}Ha$ of normal subgroup can therefore be weakened to the statement that the set of elements $a^{-1}Ha$ is contained in H.

1.8 Factor Groups

In the next section we shall consider the concepts of homomorphism and isomorphism of two groups which will lead eventually (Section 1.10) to one of the fundamental theorems in group theory. This fundamental theorem (Theorem 10) utilizes not only the concept of normal subgroup but also a derived concept, namely, that of *factor group*. In the present section we shall define and discuss factor groups.

Definition.   Let G be a group and H a normal subgroup of G.   Then the set whose elements are the cosets of H in G is called the *factor group* (or *quotient group*) of G by H.

We must, of course, first define an operation in the factor group and then show that the factor group is actually a group.   (Cf. Theorem 8.) The notation used for the factor group of G by H is G/H.   It will be seen that the notation is well chosen and that G/H has many properties analogous to those of ordinary fractions.   Here, then, is our first example of a group whose elements are themselves collections of elements of another group.

Theorem 8.   The factor group G/H of G by H is a group.

Proof: The elements of G/H are the cosets of H in G.   Group multiplication in the set G/H will be multiplication of cosets, that is $(Ha)(Hb)$ is all elements of the form $h'ah''b$, where h' and h'' are arbitrary in H. (Cf. the definition of AB given in Section 1.6.)   We first show that G/H is closed.   Let Ha and Hb be two cosets; then

$$(Ha)(Hb) = H(aH)b = H(Ha)b = HH(ab) = Hab$$

which is clearly a coset.   In the second equality we are allowed to write $aH = Ha$, since H was assumed normal.   If H were not an invariant subgroup of G, then this would not be true and G/H would not be a group

Associativity follows from the associativity in the original group G.

$$Ha[(Hb)(Hc)] = Ha(Hbc) = Ha(bc) = H(ab)c$$
$$= [(Ha)(Hb)]Hc.$$

The identity in G/H is H, since

$$H(Ha) = (Ha)H = Ha.$$

The inverse of Ha is Ha^{-1}, since

$$(Ha)(Ha^{-1}) = Ha(a^{-1}H) = H(aa^{-1})H = HeH = HH = H.$$

As an example of factor groups, consider a cyclic group G of order six :

$$G: \qquad \{e, a, a^2, a^3, a^4, a^5\}.$$

Two normal subgroups are H and K, where

$$H: \qquad \{e, a^2, a^4\},$$
$$K: \qquad \{e, a^3\}.$$

Now the elements in the factor group G/H are the cosets of H in G, namely,

$$G/H: \quad \{[\{e,a^2,a^4\}e], [\{e,a^2,a^4\}a]\}$$

or

$$G/H: \quad \{[e,a^2,a^4], [a,a^3,a^5]\}.$$

So the collections of elements $[e,a^2,a^4]$ and $[a,a^3,a^5]$ in G are the two elements of G/H. We see immediately, in general, that if the order of G is n and the order of H is m, then the order of G/H is n/m, that is, the index of H in G.

Similarly the elements in G/K are the cosets

$$\begin{aligned} K = Ke: &\quad \{e,a^3\}e = [e,a^3], \\ Ka: &\quad \{e,a^3\}a = [a,a^4], \\ Ka^2: &\quad \{e,a^3\}a^2 = [a^2,a^5], \end{aligned}$$

and

$$G/K: \quad \{[e,a^3], [a,a^4], [a^2,a^5]\}.$$

One can readily verify in these concrete instances that G/H and G/K are groups. For example, the multiplication table for G/H is

	$[e,a^2,a^4]$	$[a,a^3,a^5]$
$[e,a^2,a^4]$	$[e,a^2,a^4]$	$[a,a^3,a^5]$
$[a,a^3,a^5]$	$[a,a^3,a^5]$	$[e,a^2,a^4]$

and that of G/K is

	$[e,a^3]$	$[a,a^4]$	$[a^2,a^5]$
$[e,a^3]$	$[e,a^3]$	$[a,a^4]$	$[a^2,a^5]$
$[a,a^4]$	$[a,a^4]$	$[a^2,a^5]$	$[e,a^3]$
$[a^2,a^5]$	$[a^2,a^5]$	$[e,a^3]$	$[a,a^4]$

The factor group G/H is cyclic with $[a,a^3,a^5]$ as generator, and G/K is cyclic with $[a,a^4]$ as a generator.

In the proof of Theorem 8 we used the fact that H was normal in order to establish the group properties of G/H. It may occur to the reader that even if H is not normal, G/H might still be proved to be a group under the agreed-upon multiplication defined for factor groups. This is false. We shall give an example of a non-normal subgroup whose "factor group" is not a group.

Consider the symmetric group $\mathfrak{S}_3$ whose multiplication table appears in Section 1.4. The two elements I and T_1 form a subgroup $\mathfrak{H}$ of $\mathfrak{S}_3$, since $T_1^2 = I$.   Now $\mathfrak{H}$ is not a normal subgroup, for we shall show in particular that

$$\mathfrak{H}T_2 \neq T_2\mathfrak{H}.$$

We have

$$\mathfrak{H}T_2: \qquad \{I,T_1\}T_2 = [T_2,T_1T_2] = [T_2,T_4]$$

and

$$T_2\mathfrak{H}: \qquad T_2\{I,T_1\} = [T_2,T_2T_1] = [T_2,T_3].$$

Hence the elements of $\mathfrak{H}T_2$ and $T_2\mathfrak{H}$ are not the same.   Consider now the "factor group" $\mathfrak{S}_3/\mathfrak{H}$.   Its elements are the cosets

$$\mathfrak{H} = \mathfrak{H}I: \qquad \{I,T_1\}I = [I,T_1],$$
$$\mathfrak{H}T_2: \qquad \{I,T_1\}T_2 = [T_2,T_4],$$
$$\mathfrak{H}T_3: \qquad \{I,T_1\}T_3 = [T_3,T_5].$$

Now if $\mathfrak{S}_3/\mathfrak{H}$ is to be a group it must be closed.   But

$$(\mathfrak{H}T_2)(\mathfrak{H}T_3): \qquad [T_2,T_4][T_3,T_5] = [T_2T_3,T_2T_5,T_4T_3,T_4T_5]$$
$$= [T_1,T_4,I,T_2]$$

which is not one of the three cosets $\mathfrak{H}I$, $\mathfrak{H}T_2$, $\mathfrak{H}T_3$ and hence $\mathfrak{S}_3/\mathfrak{H}$ is not closed (and therefore there is no hope of its being a group).

1.9 Homomorphism and Isomorphism

Let S and $\bar{S}$ be two nonempty sets and let ϕ be a function which associates with every element of S a unique element of $\bar{S}$.   Such a function is called a *mapping of S into $\bar{S}$*.   We write this symbolically as

$$\phi: \qquad S \rightarrow \bar{S}.$$

If a is an element of S, then we denote the element corresponding to it in $\bar{S}$ under the mapping ϕ by $\phi(a)$ or $\bar{a}$.   We call $\phi(a)$ the *image* of a. Every element in S has a unique image by definition of ϕ; however, more than one element in S can have the same image in $\bar{S}$.   Conversely, we call a the *preimage* of $\phi(a)$ in S.   Clearly, preimages are not necessarily unique.   Since the mapping is *into*, there may exist elements in $\bar{S}$ which have no preimage in S.   If to every $\bar{b}$ in $\bar{S}$ there *does* exist an element b in S such that $\phi(b) = \bar{b}$, then we call ϕ a *mapping of S onto $\bar{S}$*.

Suppose now that ϕ is a mapping of S onto $\bar{S}$ such that every element $\bar{a}$ in $\bar{S}$ has a *unique* preimage a in S.   Then this correspondence defines a mapping of $\bar{S}$ onto S called the inverse of ϕ.   It is generally denoted by ϕ^{-1}.   Thus if $\phi(a) = \bar{a}$, then $a = \phi^{-1}(\bar{a})$.   In this case we call ϕ a *one to one mapping* and write

$$\phi: \qquad S \leftrightarrow \bar{S}.$$

If S and $\bar{S}$ are identical and ϕ is a one to one mapping which takes every element of S into itself, then we call ϕ the *identity mapping*.

With these preliminary remarks we can now define the important concepts of homomorphism and isomorphism.

Definition. Let G and $\bar{G}$ be groups with respective binary operations $*$ and $\circ$. Let ϕ be a mapping of G into $\bar{G}$,

$$\phi: \quad G \to \bar{G}.$$

If this mapping has the property that

$$\phi(a*b) = \phi(a) \circ \phi(b)$$

for all a, b in G, then we call ϕ a *homomorphism*. Suppose further that ϕ is a one to one mapping of G onto $\bar{G}$ such that

$$\phi(a*b) = \phi(a) \circ \phi(b)$$

for all a, b in G. Then we call ϕ an *isomorphism*. We say G and $\bar{G}$ are *isomorphic* if there exists an isomorphism ϕ mapping G onto $\bar{G}$.

As we have done frequently in the past, we omit the symbols $*$ and $\circ$ and write the above equation simply as

$$\phi(ab) = \phi(a)\phi(b),$$

where the appropriate binary operation indicated on each side of this equation is understood.

Certain immediate inferences can be drawn from the definition itself. First we note that if e is the identity in G, then $\phi(e)$ is the identity in $\bar{G}$. This follows immediately from the equation

$$\phi(a) = \phi(ae) = \phi(a)\phi(e),$$

where a is an element in G. Also we note that $\phi(a^{-1})$ is the inverse of $\phi(a)$, that is, $\phi(a^{-1}) = \phi(a)^{-1}$. This remark follows at once from

$$\phi(e) = \phi(aa^{-1}) = \phi(a)\phi(a^{-1}).$$

However, before proving various important theorems involving homomorphisms and isomorphisms, we shall present several examples.

A. Let G be a group. Let I be the identity subgroup of G, that is, the subgroup consisting of the identity e in G alone. Let ϕ be a mapping which takes every element of G into e,

$$\phi: \quad G \to I.$$

We assert that ϕ is a homomorphism.   For, let a and b be any two elements in G.   Then

$$\phi(ab) = e = ee = \phi(a)\phi(b)$$

by definition of ϕ.

B. Let G consist of all pairs of real numbers $\{a_1,a_2\}$.   Define the binary operation as

$$\{a_1,a_2\} + \{b_1,b_2\} = \{a_1 + b_1,\, a_2 + b_2\}.$$

Clearly G is closed and associative by virtue of the corresponding properties of real numbers.   The identity element is $\{0,0\}$ and the inverse of $\{a_1,a_2\}$ is $\{-a_1, -a_2\}$.   Hence G is a group.   Note that in the above equation the plus sign on the left stands for "group multiplication," while the plus signs on the right stand for ordinary addition of real numbers.

Now let $\bar{G}$ consist of the totality of real numbers.   We know that $\bar{G}$ is a group under addition.   Establish a mapping ϕ of G onto $\bar{G}$ by

$$\phi: \qquad \{a_1,a_2\} \to a_1.$$

Then ϕ is a homomorphism, since

$$\phi(\{a_1,a_2\} + \{b_1,b_2\}) = \phi(\{a_1 + b_1,\, a_2 + b_2\})$$
$$= a_1 + b_1 = \phi(\{a_1,a_2\}) + \phi(\{b_1,b_2\}).$$

It is not an isomorphism, for many elements in G are mapped onto a single element of $\bar{G}$.   Geometrically we can think of G as being the totality of two-dimensional vectors in the plane emanating from the origin.   Then ϕ is the projection of every vector on the X-axis.

If we consider in G the totality of elements of the form $\{a,0\}$ we see that they form a proper subgroup of G.   For example, this subgroup, say H, is closed, since $\{a,0\} + \{b,0\} = \{a + b,\, 0\}$ which is in H.   This subgroup H is *isomorphic* to $\bar{G}$ under the mapping

$$\psi: \qquad \{a,0\} \leftrightarrow a.$$

We can "identify $\bar{G}$ with H" and use the simple symbol a in place of $\{a,0\}$ in the group G.   For example, the equation

$$\{a_1,a_2\} + \{b_1,0\} = \{a_1 + b_1,\, a_2\}$$

in G could be written

$$\{a_1,a_2\} + b_1 = \{a_1 + b_1,\, a_2\}.$$

Perhaps unknowingly the reader has already performed such identifications of isomorphic sets in elementary mathematics.   For example, consider the totality of complex numbers $a + ib$. Their law of addition is identical with that in G, namely,

$$(a + ib) + (c + id) = (a + c) + i(b + d).$$

Now the totality of complex numbers with zero imaginary part, that is, numbers of the form $a + i0$ form a subset of the totality of complex numbers and are isomorphic (under addition) to the totality of real numbers. We never write $a + i0$, but always simply a, that is, the corresponding element from the isomorphic set.

C. Let Z be the group of integers $\{0, \pm 1, \pm 2, \cdots\}$ with addition as the binary operation. Let p be a positive integer and let S_0 consist of all integers which are divisible by p, and let S_1 consist of all integers which are divisible by p with a remainder of one, etc., up to S_{p-1}, which consists of all integers which are divisible by p with a remainder of $p - 1$. In other words, S_i consists of all integers n such that $n \equiv i$ (mod p), that is, such that $n - i$ is divisible by p. Now consider the set $\bar{Z}$ which consists of the p elements

$$S_0, S_1, \cdots, S_{p-1}.$$

We define a binary operation $+$ in $\bar{Z}$ by the relation

$$S_i + S_j = S_k$$

if $i + j$ is divisible by p with a remainder of k. It will be left as an exercise for the reader to show that under this binary operation $\bar{Z}$ is a group.

We assert that the mapping ϕ of Z onto $\bar{Z}$ defined by

$$\phi: \qquad n \to S_k$$

where $n - k$ is divisible by p is a homomorphism. To be even more concrete, let $p = 3$, Then,

$$\{0, 3, 6, 9, \cdots, -3, -6, -9, \cdots\} = S_0$$
$$\{1, 4, 7, 10, \cdots, -2, -5, -8, \cdots\} = S_1$$
$$\{2, 5, 8, 11, \cdots, -1, -4, -7, \cdots\} = S_2.$$

Clearly

	S_0	S_1	S_2
S_0	S_0	S_1	S_2
S_1	S_1	S_2	S_0
S_2	S_2	S_0	S_1

is a multiplication table for $\bar{Z}$. If n and m are integers,

$$n = 3q_1 + r_1, \qquad 0 \leq r_1 < 3$$
$$m = 3q_2 + r_2, \qquad 0 \leq r_2 < 3$$
$$m + n = 3q_3 + r_3, \qquad 0 \leq r_3 < 3$$

and $r_1 + r_2$ differs from r_3 by a multiple of 3. Hence

$$\phi(n + m) = S_{r_3}$$
$$\phi(n) + \phi(m) = S_{r_1} + S_{r_2} = S_{r_3}$$

and ϕ is a homomorphism.

D. Let Z be the group of integers $\{0, \pm 1, \pm 2, \cdots\}$ under addition and let Z' be the group of powers of 2, $\{1, 2^{\pm 1}, 2^{\pm 2}, \cdots\}$ under multiplication. Let the one to one mapping be

$$\phi: \qquad n \leftrightarrow 2^n.$$

Clearly ϕ is an isomorphism, for from

$$n + m = p$$

follows

$$2^n \cdot 2^m = 2^p,$$

and conversely.

E. Let G be the group $\{0, 1, 2, 3, 4, 5, 6\}$ under addition modulo seven. Let G' be a cyclic group of order seven, $\{e, a, a^2, a^3, a^4, a^5, a^6\}$. Then under the mapping

$$n \leftrightarrow a^n$$

G and G' are isomorphic, for from

$$n + m \equiv p \pmod{7}$$

follows

$$a^n \cdot a^m = a^{n+m} = a^p.$$

F. On the other hand, the group G of order six

$$\{1, 2, 3, 4, 5, 6\}$$

under multiplication modulo seven is isomorphic to the cyclic group

$$\{e, a, a^2, a^3, a^4, a^5\}$$

of order six, but is not isomorphic to the symmetric group $\mathfrak{S}_3$ of order six. (Cf. Example A of Section 1.4 for the multiplication table of $\mathfrak{S}_3$.)

no 1/1 correspondance

G. Also the two possible groups of order four (cf. Exercise 1.6) whose multiplication tables are

	e	a	b	c
e	e	a	b	c
a	a	b	c	e
b	b	c	e	a
c	c	e	a	b

and

	e	a	b	c
e	e	a	b	c
a	a	e	c	b
b	b	c	e	a
c	c	b	a	e

are not isomorphic.

If two groups G and $\bar{G}$ are isomorphic we sometimes use the notation

$$G \approx \bar{G}$$

to indicate this fact. The equation "$G \approx \bar{G}$" is read "G is isomorphic to $\bar{G}$." To be more explicit we should mention the mapping since it is possible for two groups to be isomorphic under more than one mapping. For example, the set of all complex numbers under addition is a group which is isomorphic to itself under the identity mapping as well as the mapping which takes every number into its complex conjugate.

We conclude this section with a theorem on *homomorphic images*. Let G and $\bar{G}$ be groups and let ϕ be a homomorphic mapping of G onto $\bar{G}$. Then $\bar{G}$ is called a *homomorphic image* of G.

Theorem 9. Let ϕ be a homomorphic mapping of G into $\bar{G}$. Let $\bar{H}$ be the homomorphic image of G in $\bar{G}$. Then $\bar{H}$ is a subgroup of $\bar{G}$.

Proof: Let $\bar{a}$ and $\bar{b}$ be any two elements in $\bar{H}$. Let a and b be any preimages of $\bar{a}$ and $\bar{b}$, respectively, in G. Under the homomorphism ϕ,

$$\phi(ab) = \phi(a)\phi(b).$$

Since ab is an element of G, $\phi(ab)$ is in $\bar{H}$ and $\bar{H}$ is closed. The associativity follows immediately since $\bar{H}$ is a subset of $\bar{G}$. If e is the identity of G, then $\phi(e)$, the identity in $\bar{G}$ is in $\bar{H}$. If $\bar{a}$ is in $\bar{H}$ and a is a preimage in G, then a^{-1} is in G. Thus $\phi(a^{-1})$ is in $\bar{H}$ since $\bar{H}$ is the homomorphic image of G. But we have shown that

$$\phi(a^{-1}) = \phi(a)^{-1}.$$

Hence $\phi(a)^{-1}$, the inverse of $\phi(a)$, is in $\bar{H}$.

1.10. A Fundamental Theorem

We are now in a position to state and prove the important theorem mentioned in Section 1.8, namely,

Theorem 10.   Let ϕ be a homomorphism mapping G onto $\bar{G}$.   Let H be the set of elements in G which map onto the identity $\bar{e}$ of $\bar{G}$.   Then H is a normal subgroup of G and the factor group G/H is isomorphic to $\bar{G}$.

Proof: (i) H is a group.

Suppose a and b are arbitrary elements in H.   Then

$$\phi(ab) = \phi(a)\phi(b) = \bar{e}\bar{e} = \bar{e}$$

and H is closed.   The associativity is evident; the identity is in H, since $\phi(e) = \bar{e}$.   If a is in H, then from the equation

$$\bar{e} = \bar{e}^{-1} = [\phi(a)]^{-1} = \phi(a^{-1})$$

we conclude a^{-1} is in H.

(ii) H is a normal subgroup.

Let g be an arbitrary element in G and let h be any element in H. Let $k = g^{-1}hg$.   Now k is in H, since

$$\phi(k) = \phi(g^{-1}hg) = \phi(g^{-1})\phi(h)\phi(g) = \phi(g^{-1})\bar{e}\phi(g) = \phi(g^{-1})\phi(g)$$
$$= \phi(g^{-1}g) = \phi(e) = \bar{e}$$

and thus H is normal.

(iii) G/H is isomorphic to $\bar{G}$.

The mapping will be

$$\psi: \qquad Ha \leftrightarrow \bar{a}.$$

We shall first show that ψ is one to one.   (a) If $Ha = Hb$ and $Ha \to \bar{a}$, $Hb \to \bar{b}$; then $\bar{a} = \bar{b}$: Since $Ha = Hb$, this implies $b = ha$ for some h in H and under the homomorphism ϕ, $\bar{b} = \bar{h}\bar{a} = \bar{e}\bar{a} = \bar{a}$.   Hence every coset of H in G is mapped onto at most one element of $\bar{G}$.   (b) We must now show that if $\bar{a} = \bar{b}$ and $\bar{a} \to Ha$, $\bar{b} \to Hb$, then $Ha = Hb$: Consider the element $k = ab^{-1}$ in G.   Then $\phi(k) = \phi(ab^{-1}) = \phi(a)\phi(b^{-1})$ $= \phi(a)\phi(a^{-1}) = \phi(e) = \bar{e}$.   Thus k is in H.   Hence $a = kb$ and $Ha = H(kb) = (Hk)b = Hb$.   Thus we have a one to one correspondence among the elements (cosets) of G/H and the elements of $\bar{G}$.

To show that ψ is an isomorphism, we need only write

$$\psi(\bar{a}\bar{b}) = Hab = (Ha)(Hb) = \psi(\bar{a})\psi(\bar{b}). \qquad (1.8)$$

Hence the desired isomorphism has been established and the theorem is proved.

In the above theorem we see that there is a "natural" homomorphism of G onto G/H by the mapping $a \to Ha$. We now generalize this idea and give a technical definition to the phrase "natural homomorphism."

Theorem 11. Let G be a group, H a normal subgroup of G, and G/H the factor group of G by H. Let ν be the mapping

$$\nu : \quad a \to Ha,$$

of G onto G/H. Then ν is a homomorphism.

Proof: If a and b are arbitrary elements in G, then

$$\nu(ab) = H(ab) = (Ha)(Hb) = \nu(a)\nu(b)$$

which proves that ν is a homomorphism.

The homomorphic mapping

$$\nu : \quad G \to G/H$$

defined above will be called the *natural homomorphism* of G onto G/H.

Note   Homomorphism is a transitive relation. Roughly speaking, if ϕ and ψ are homomorphisms, then so is $\psi\phi$. The precise statement is:

Theorem 12. Let ϕ be a homomorphism mapping G onto G' and let ψ be a homomorphism mapping G' onto G''. Then $\psi\phi$ is a homomorphism of G onto G''.

Proof: First we define $\psi\phi$. Suppose a is an element in G; then $\phi(a) = a'$ is an element in G' and $\psi(a') = a''$ is an element in G''. We define $\psi\phi$ as the mapping which takes a into a'',

$$\psi\phi(a) = a''.$$

Now let a and b be arbitrary elements in G. Then

$$\phi(ab) = \phi(a)\phi(b),$$

since ϕ is a homomorphism, where $\phi(a)$ and $\phi(b)$ are elements in G'. Also

$$\psi(\phi(a)\phi(b)) = \psi(\phi(a))\psi(\phi(b))$$

since ψ is also a homomorphism. The last two equations imply

$$\psi(\phi(ab)) = \psi(\phi(a))\psi(\phi(b)) \tag{1.9}$$

or

$$\psi\phi(ab) = \psi\phi(a)\psi\phi(b). \quad \text{by def of operation}$$

1.11 Maximal Subgroups

In order to develop our theory further in the most convenient manner we must introduce certain additional terminology and definitions. If A and B are two arbitrary sets, then we shall use the symbol $A \subset B$ to mean *proper inclusion*. By this we mean that every element in A is in B (but not conversely). We say A is a *subset* of B. By the symbol $A \subseteq B$ we shall mean that A is a subset of B where equality is not excluded. A similar definition holds for $\supset$ and $\supseteq$. If $A \subseteq B$ and $A \supseteq B$, then clearly $A = B$, that is, every element of A is in B and conversely (cf. Section 1.6). The symbols $\subset$, $\subseteq$, $\supset$, $\supseteq$ when applied to sets are analogous to the symbols $<$, $\leqq$, $>$, $\geqq$ as applied to real numbers. While we have defined inclusion for arbitrary sets, our applications in the immediate future will be to the cases where both A and B are groups. Another useful concept is that of the *intersection* of two sets A and B, which is written $A \cap B$. By this we mean the totality of elements common to *both* A and B.

An important notion is that of a maximal subgroup. We shall say that a normal subgroup H of a group G is *maximal* if there exists no proper normal subgroup K of G which properly contains H. Sometimes, for emphasis, we say H is a *maximal invariant* subgroup of G. If H is maximal in G, then clearly there exists no normal subgroup K of G with the property

$$G \supset K \supset H.$$

A group may contain more than one maximal subgroup as we shall see later by example.

We are leading up to a very important theorem in group theory known as the Jordan-Hölder theorem (cf. Section 1.12). However, the preliminary theorems which we shall prove in this section are also interesting in themselves.

Theorem 13. Let G be a group and H a normal subgroup of G. If there exists a normal subgroup K with $G \supset K \supset H$, then the factor group K/H is a normal subgroup of the factor group G/H. Conversely, if K/H is a normal subgroup of G/H, then K is a normal subgroup of G.

Proof: Since H is a normal subgroup of G it is certainly a normal subgroup of K. Hence K/H *is* a group. We shall show that K/H is normal. Let Hg be any element in G/H and let Hk be any element in K/H, where k is arbitrary in K and g is arbitrary in G. All we need show to prove K/H is normal is that

$$(Hg)^{-1}(Hk)(Hg)$$

is an element in K/H. Now,

$$(Hg)^{-1}(Hk)(Hg) = (g^{-1}H^{-1})(Hk)(Hg) = Hg^{-1}HkHg$$
$$= HHHg^{-1}kg = Hg^{-1}kg.$$

Clearly $g^{-1}kg$ is in K, since K is normal. Hence $H(g^{-1}kg)$ is in K/H and K/H is normal.

Conversely, let Hk be any element in K/H and let Hg be any element in G/H. In order to prove that K is normal we must show that $g^{-1}kg$ is in K. Now since H is normal in G,

$$(Hg)^{-1}(Hk)(Hg) = Hg^{-1}kg,$$

and $Hg^{-1}kg$ is an element in K/H by hypothesis. Since all elements in K/H are of the form Hx, where x is an element in K, we conclude that $g^{-1}kg$ is an element in K. This proves that K is normal.

Corollary. If every normal subgroup of G/H is of the form K/H, then H is maximal in G if and only if G/H is simple.

(We recall, cf. Section 1.7, that a group is simple if it has no proper normal subgroups.)

Proof: Suppose H is maximal and G/H is not simple. Let K/H be an invariant subgroup of G/H. Then, by the previous theorem,

$$G \supset K \supset H,$$

which contradicts the statement that H is maximal in G.

Conversely, suppose G/H is simple and H is not maximal. Since H is not maximal there exists a normal subgroup K such that $G \supset K \supset H$ and by the previous theorem, $G/H \supset K/H \supset H/H = I$, where K/H is a normal subgroup of G/H. This contradicts the assumption that G/H is simple.

After these preliminary results we prove the following theorem which is crucial in the proof of the Jordan-Hölder theorem.

Theorem 14. If G is a group and H and K are distinct maximal invariant subgroups of G, then their intersection $D = H \cap K$ is a normal subgroup of G; the factor groups G/H and K/D are isomorphic, $G/H \approx K/D$ as well as the factor groups G/K and H/D, $G/K \approx H/D$.

Proof: (i) D is a group.

We shall show that D satisfies the four group axioms. Suppose d_1 and d_2 are two elements in D. Then, since D is a subset of both H and K, both d_1 and d_2 are in both H and K. Since H is a group, d_1d_2 is in H, and since K is a group, d_1d_2 is in K. Hence, since d_1d_2 is in both H and K, it is in D. The set D is therefore closed. Since D is a subset of G, it obeys the associative law. The identity e is in D since e is in both

H and K. If d is in D, then d is in both H and K, and by the group property of H and K, d^{-1} is also in both H and K and therefore in D.

(ii) D is an invariant subgroup of G.

We must show that all elements of the form $g^{-1}dg$, where d is any element in D and g is arbitrary in G, are in D. Now since D is a subgroup of H, d is in H, and since H is normal, $g^{-1}dg$ is in H. Similarly $g^{-1}dg$ is in K. Therefore $g^{-1}dg$ is in the intersection of H and K, namely, D.

Another fact we shall need in the proof of our theorem is:

(iii) HK is a normal subgroup of G.

We first prove HK is a group. Let h_1k_1 and h_2k_2 be any two elements in HK. We shall show that

$$(h_1k_1)(h_2k_2) = hk$$

for some h in H and some k in K. Since H is normal, $k_1h_2k_1^{-1}$ is an element in H, say h_3. Hence

$$k_1h_2k_1^{-1} = h_3$$

or, on multiplying on the right by k_1,

$$k_1h_2 = h_3k_1.$$

Hence

$$(h_1k_1)(h_2k_2) = h_1(k_1h_2)k_2 = h_1(h_3k_1)k_2 = (h_1h_3)(k_1k_2).$$

Since H and K are closed, $h_1h_3 = h$, $k_1k_2 = k$, where h and k are in H and K, respectively. The associativity is obvious, since HK is a subset of G. The identity e is in HK, since e is in H, e is in K, and $e = ee$ is in HK. If hk is in HK we shall show that $(hk)^{-1}$ is in HK. Since H is normal, $k^{-1}h^{-1}k$ is some element in H, say h'. Therefore

$$(hk)^{-1} = k^{-1}h^{-1} = h'k^{-1}$$

which is an element in HK.

To show that HK is invariant, we must show that

$$g^{-1}(hk)g$$

is an element in HK for every h in H, k in K, and g in G. Now

$$g^{-1}(hk)g = g^{-1}(hek)g = (g^{-1}h)(gg^{-1})(kg) = (g^{-1}hg)(g^{-1}kg).$$

But H and K are normal; hence $g^{-1}hg$ is in H, say h' and $g^{-1}kg$ is in K, say k'. Hence

$$g^{-1}(hk)g = h'k',$$

which is an element in HK.

(iv) $HK = G$.

The normal subgroup HK includes H properly,

$$H \subset HK.$$

First, $H \subseteq HK$ since e is in K and $H = He$. Also we assert H is *properly* contained in HK. By hypothesis H and K are distinct and hence there exists a k in K which is not in H. Therefore $ek = k$ is an element of HK which is not in H.

Now suppose HK is not equal to G. Then we would have

$$H \subset HK \subset G.$$

But H is maximal in G, and HK properly contains H. Hence $HK = G$.

We now proceed to establish the desired isomorphism appearing in the statement of the theorem. Since D is a subgroup of K we can decompose K according to cosets of D:

$$K = D + Da + Db + \cdots. \tag{1.10}$$

We assert that

$$HK = HD + (HD)a + (HD)b + \cdots$$

is also a true equation with the same $a, b, \cdots$ as above. First, if hk is an element on the left-hand side of this equation, then by Equation 1.10, k appears in some coset, say Dx, and hence hk is in $(HD)x$. Therefore,

$$HK \subseteq HD + (HD)a + (HD)b + \cdots.$$

But $G = HK$ by (iv) above, and hence

$$HK \supseteq HD + (HD)a + (HD)b + \cdots.$$

Also, $HD = H$, since D is a subgroup of H. Therefore we have

$$G = H + Ha + Hb + \cdots \tag{1.11}$$

We must show now that the above equation is a decomposition of G according to cosets of H in G (that is, that there are not two identical cosets in Equation 1.11). Suppose that $Ha = Hb$; then $ha = h'b$ and $ab^{-1} = h^{-1}h' = h''$ is an element in H. By Equation 1.10, a and b are in K and hence ab^{-1} is in K. Since ab^{-1} is in both H and K, it is in D and therefore $Da = Db$, which contradicts the fact that Equation 1.10 is a decomposition of K according to cosets of D in K. Hence Equation 1.11 is a representation of G according to distinct cosets of H in G.

The elements of the factor group K/D are

$$D, Da, Db, \cdots$$

and those of G/H are

$$H, Ha, Hb, \cdots$$

Let ψ be the one to one mapping of K/D onto G/H which sets up a correspondence between D and H, Da and Ha, etc. Now

$$\psi(DxDy) = \psi(Dxy) = Hxy = (Hx)(Hy) = \psi(Dx)\psi(Dy).$$

Hence ψ is an isomorphism.

In a similar fashion we prove that G/K is isomorphic to H/D.

As an example of the above theorem, let G be a cyclic group of order 30 with generator a:

$$G: \quad \{e, a, a^2, a^3, \cdots, a^{28}, a^{29}\}.$$

Let H and K be

$$H: \quad \{e, a^2, a^4, \cdots, a^{28}\}$$
$$K: \quad \{e, a^3, a^6, \cdots, a^{27}\}.$$

Clearly H and K are subgroups of G of orders 15 and 10, respectively. H and K are also normal, since G is abelian. H is maximal in G, for if it were not, there would exist a subgroup of order q, $30 > q > 15$. But q must divide 30 and 15 must divide q, since the order of a subgroup divides the order of the group. Clearly there exists no integer q with this property. Similarly K is also a maximal subgroup of G. The two maximal subgroups H and K are distinct and their intersection D is

$$D: \quad \{e, a^6, a^{12}, a^{18}, a^{24}\}.$$

The factor group G/H has the elements H, Ha^3—or, more conventionally,

$$G/H: \quad \{H, Ha\},$$

and the factor group K/D has the elements

$$K/D: \quad \{D, Da^3\}.$$

Under the mapping

$$H \leftrightarrow D$$
$$Ha \leftrightarrow Da^3,$$

K/D and G/H are isomorphic, since

$$(Da^3)(Da^3) = Da^6 = D$$

and

$$(Ha)(Ha) = Ha^2 = H.$$

Also the factor group, G/K,

$$G/K: \quad \{K, Ka, Ka^2\}$$

is isomorphic to the factor group H/D,

$$H/D: \quad \{D, Da^2, Da^4\}$$

under the mapping

$$K \leftrightarrow D$$
$$Ka \leftrightarrow Da^2$$
$$Ka^2 \leftrightarrow Da^4.$$

The reader may construct the multiplication tables of G/K and H/D to verify this concrete example.

1.12 The Jordan-Hölder Theorem

This section will be devoted to the proof of the Jordan-Hölder theorem, which is one of the major theorems in the elementary theory of groups. We shall prove it for the case of finite groups. A slightly more general theorem is the so-called Jordan-Hölder-Schreier theorem, a proof of which may be found in Zassenhaus, *The Theory of Groups*.

Definition. If G is a group we call a finite sequence of subgroups

$$G = H_0, H_1, \cdots, H_r = I$$

a *composition series* if each H_i is a maximal invariant subgroup of H_{i-1}.

If G is a cyclic group of order, six,

$$G : \quad \{e, a, a^2, a^3, a^4, a^5\},$$

then

$$G = \{e, a, a^2, a^3, a^4, a^5\}, \quad H = \{e, a^3\}, \quad I = \{e\}$$

and

$$G = \{e, a, a^2, a^3, a^4, a^5\}, \quad K = \{e, a^2, a^4\}, \quad I = \{e\}$$

are two composition series for G. (K is maximal in G, for if it were not, there would exist a group K_1 of order q, $6 > q > 3$, between G and K. Clearly no number q which divides 6 and is divisible by 3 has this property. Similarly, H is maximal in G, I is maximal in K, and I is maximal in H.)

It is not immediately obvious that an arbitrary abstract group *has* a composition series. In fact, if G is an infinite cyclic group,

$$G : \quad \{e, a^{\pm 1}, a^{\pm 2}, a^{\pm 3}, \cdots\}$$

and H is any (normal) subgroup, for example,

$$H : \quad \{e, a^{\pm p}, a^{\pm 2p}, a^{\pm 3p}, \cdots\}$$

where p is any integer, then there always exists a normal subgroup between H and I, for example,

$$K : \quad \{e, a^{\pm 2p}, a^{\pm 4p}, a^{\pm 6p}, \cdots\}$$

is such a subgroup.   However, for *finite* groups we have the following theorem.

   Theorem 15.   Every finite group G possesses at least one composition series.

   Proof: If G is simple,

$$G, I$$

is a composition series.   Suppose G is not simple.   Then there exists a proper normal subgroup H of G.   If H is maximal in G, and I is maximal in H, then

$$G, H, I$$

is a composition series.   Suppose H is not maximal in G.   Then there exists a normal subgroup K such that

$$G \supset K \supset H.$$

If K is maximal in G and H is maximal in K, then

$$G, K, H, I$$

is a composition series.   Similarly, if I is not maximal in H there exists a subgroup L such that

$$G \supset K \supset H \supset L \supset I.$$

If L is maximal in H and I is maximal in L, then

$$G, K, H, L, I$$

is a composition series.   Since G is finite, there can exist at most a finite number of subgroups in the composition series, since each subgroup is a proper subgroup of the next larger group.

   After these many preliminaries, we are in a position to state and prove the Jordan-Hölder theorem.

   Jordan-Hölder Theorem.   (Theorem 16).   Let G be a finite group with two composition series *are of same order + factor groups are 1-1*

$$G = H_0, H_1, \cdots, H_r = I$$
$$G = K_0, K_1, \cdots, K_s = I.$$

Then $r = s$ and the factor groups

$$H_0/H_1, H_1/H_2, \cdots, H_{r-1}/H_r$$
$$K_0/K_1, K_1/K_2, \cdots, K_{s-1}/K_s$$

may be put into one to one correspondence such that corresponding factor groups are isomorphic.

must have same # of groups

Proof: Let n be the order of G. Let the number of primes which appear in the factorization of n be ω, that is,

$$n = p_1 p_2 \ldots p_\omega.$$

The prime numbers p_i appearing in the above factorization are not necessarily distinct. Our proof will proceed by complete induction on ω.

(i) If $\omega = 0$, $G = I$ and the theorem is trivial.

(ii) If $\omega = 1$, $n = p_1$, and G is of prime order. Therefore G has no proper subgroups and

$$G, I$$

is the only composition series.

(iii) We shall now suppose that the theorem has been established for $\omega = 0, 1, \cdots, k$. Let G be any group whose order contains $k + 1$ prime factors. Two cases arise.

(a) G is simple.

In this case there is but one composition series,

$$G, I$$

and the theorem is trivial.

(b) G is not simple.

Then there exists at least one composition series of length greater than two. If this series is unique, the theorem is trivial. Suppose it is not unique. Then we have two distinct composition series of length greater than two, say

$$G = H_0, H_1, \cdots, H_r = I \tag{1.12}$$

and

$$G = K_0, K_1, \cdots, K_s = I. \tag{1.13}$$

Two cases again arise, either $H_1 = K_1$ or $H_1 \neq K_1$. Suppose $H_1 = K_1$. Then the theorem follows by the induction hypothesis, since the order of H_1 contains k or fewer prime factors. Suppose $H_1 \neq K_1$. Let D be the intersection of H_1 and K_1 and consider the sequences

$$G, H_1, D, D_1, \cdots, D_t \tag{1.14}$$

$$G, K_1, D, D'_1, \cdots, D'_t \tag{1.15}$$

where $D, D_1, \cdots, D_t$ and $D, D'_1, \cdots, D'_t$ are two composition series for D. If we can show D is maximal in H_1 and K_1, then Equations 1.14 and 1.15 will be composition series for G. By Theorem 14, $G/H_1 \approx K_1/D$. The group H_1 is maximal in G by construction and hence by the corollary to Theorem 13, G/H_1 is simple. Therefore K_1/D is simple and by the same corollary D is maximal in K_1. Similarly D is maximal in H_1. Hence Equations 1.14 and 1.15 are two composition series. Now the theorem holds for the sequences of Equations 1.14 and 1.15, since $G/H_1 \approx K_1/D$, $H_1/D \approx G/K_1$, and the order of D contains fewer than k prime factors. The theorem also holds for the composition series of Equations 1.12 and 1.14, since $G/H_1 = G/H_1$ and the order of H_1 contains k or fewer prime factors. Similarly the theorem holds for the composition series of Equations 1.13 and 1.15. Hence by Theorem 12 the Jordan-Hölder theorem is true for the composition series of Equations 1.12 and 1.13. This concludes the proof.

As an example of the Jordan-Hölder theorem, let G be a cyclic group of order 30 with generator a.

$$G: \quad \{e, a, a^2, a^3, \cdots, a^{28}, a^{29}\}.$$

The only subgroups of G other than G itself are

$$
\begin{aligned}
G_{15}: &\quad \{e, a^2, a^4, \cdots, a^{26}, a^{28}\} \\
G_{10}: &\quad \{e, a^3, a^6, \cdots, a^{24}, a^{27}\} \\
G_6: &\quad \{e, a^5, a^{10}, a^{15}, a^{20}, a^{25}\} \\
G_5: &\quad \{e, a^6, a^{12}, a^{18}, a^{24}\} \\
G_3: &\quad \{e, a^{10}, a^{20}\} \\
G_2: &\quad \{e, a^{15}\} \\
I = G_1: &\quad \{e\}
\end{aligned}
$$

where the subscript on the G's indicates the order of the group. Since G is cyclic, all the subgroups are normal. With these subgroups we can construct the following sequences where each group is a subgroup of the group to its left.

$$G, G_{15}, G_5, G_1 \tag{1.16}$$
$$G, G_{15}, G_3, G_1$$
$$G, G_{10}, G_5, G_1$$
$$G, G_{10}, G_2, G_1$$
$$G, G_6, \ G_3, G_1 \tag{1.17}$$
$$G, G_6, \ G_2, G_1.$$

Since there exist no subgroups between any two consecutive groups in any of the above sequences, there obviously exist no maximal subgroups with this property. Hence each of the above sequences is a composition series. The factor groups of Equation 1.16 are

$$
\begin{aligned}
G/G_{15}: &\quad \{G_{15}, aG_{15}\} \\
G_{15}/G_5: &\quad \{G_5, a^2G_5, a^4G_5\} \\
G_5/G_1: &\quad \{G_1, a^6G_1, a^{12}G_1, a^{18}G_1, a^{24}G_1\}
\end{aligned}
$$

and those of Equation 1.17 are

$$G/G_6: \quad \{G_6, aG_6, a^2G_6, a^3G_6, a^4G_6\}$$
$$G_6/G_3: \quad \{G_3, a^5G_3\}$$
$$G_3/G_1: \quad \{G_1, a^{10}G_1, a^{20}G_1\}.$$

Clearly,

$$G/G_{15} \approx G_6/G_3$$
$$G_{15}/G_5 \approx G_3/G_1$$
$$G_5/G_1 \approx G/G_6$$

under the mappings

$$G_{15} \leftrightarrow G_3$$
$$aG_{15} \leftrightarrow a^5G_3,$$

$$G_5 \leftrightarrow G_1$$
$$a^2G_5 \leftrightarrow a^{10}G_1$$
$$a^4G_5 \leftrightarrow a^{20}G_1$$

and

$$G_1 \leftrightarrow G_6$$
$$a^6G_1 \leftrightarrow aG_6$$
$$a^{12}G_1 \leftrightarrow a^2G_6$$
$$a^{18}G_1 \leftrightarrow a^3G_6$$
$$a^{24}G_1 \leftrightarrow a^4G_6$$

respectively, as may be verified by constructing the multiplication tables for the factor groups. For example,

	G_5	a^2G_5	a^4G_5
G_5	G_5	a^2G_5	a^4G_5
a^2G_5	a^2G_5	a^4G_5	G_5
a^4G_5	a^4G_5	G_5	a^2G_5

is the multiplication table for G_{15}/G_5 and

	G_1	$a^{10}G_1$	$a^{20}G_1$
G_1	G_1	$a^{10}G_1$	$a^{20}G_1$
$a^{10}G_1$	$a^{10}G_1$	$a^{20}G_1$	G_1
$a^{20}G_1$	$a^{20}G_1$	G_1	$a^{10}G_1$

is the multiplication table for G_3/G_1.

We leave as an exercise for the reader the verification of the fact that any other pair of the above five composition series satisfies the Jordan-Hölder theorem.

1.13 Direct Products

If we are given two abstract groups G and H we may form the totality of all pairs (g,h), where g is an element in G and h is an element in H. When a suitable binary operation is defined, these pairs (g,h) will be shown to form a group called the *direct product* of G by H and written $G \times H$. Note that $G \times H$ is not the same as GH, for GH was defined as all products of the form gh where g was in G and h was in H (both G and H being subgroups of the same group). Also, $G \times H$ is not necessarily the same as $H \times G$.

We define a binary operation $*$ in $G \times H$ by the equation

$$(g,h)*(g',h') = (gg',hh') \tag{1.18}$$

where g, g' are in G, and h, h' are in H. Note that in forming gg' we use the group multiplication defined in G, while in writing hh' we use the group multiplication defined in H. Hence in writing Equation 1.18, three different binary operations have been utilized. As in previous developments, it will be found convenient to drop the $*$ and simply write

$$(g,h)(g',h') = (gg',hh').$$

The proof that $G \times H$ is a group is trivial:

Closure. Clearly gg' is in G and hh' is in H, since G and H are groups.

Associativity.

$$(g,h)[(g',h')(g'',h'')] = (g(g'g''),\ h(h'h''))$$
$$= ((gg')g'',\ (hh')h'') = [(g,h)(g',h')](g'',h'').$$

Identity. If e_G is the identity in G and e_H is the identity in H, then (e_G,e_H) is the identity in $G \times H$ for

$$(e_G,e_H)(g,h) = (e_G g, e_H h) = (g,h)$$

for any g in G, h in H.

Inverse. The inverse $(g,h)^{-1}$ of (g,h) is (g^{-1},h^{-1}), since

$$(g^{-1},h^{-1})(g,h) = (g^{-1}g, h^{-1}h) = (e_G,e_H).$$

As an example, consider the two groups Z and M, where Z is the totality of integers under addition and M is the multiplicative group of the four fourth roots of unity. Then, for example,

$$(p,i)(n, -i) = (p + n,\ i(-i)) = (p + n, +1)$$

where p and n are integers (elements in Z) and i is $\sqrt{-1}$ (an element in M). Hence we have an example of two groups, one infinite, the other finite, with different binary operations in each. The identity is $(0,1)$ since

$$(p,a)(0,1) = (p + 0, a \cdot 1) = (p,a)$$

where p is an integer (in Z) and a is in M ($a = 1, -1, i, -i$). The inverse of (p,a), namely, $(p,a)^{-1}$, is $(-p, a^{-1})$. For example,

$$(p,i)^{-1} = (-p, i^{-1}) \equiv (-p, -i)$$

since

$$(p,i)(-p, i^{-1}) = (p - p, ii^{-1}) = (0,1).$$

An elementary theorem on direct products is the following:

Theorem 17. If G and H are abstract groups, then the direct product $G \times H$ contains a subgroup isomorphic to G and a subgroup isomorphic to H.

Proof: The totality of elements of the form (g,e_H), where g is arbitrary in G, forms a subgroup K of $G \times H$. The set K is closed, since

$$(g,e_H)(g',e_H) = (gg',e_He_H) = (g'',e_H)$$

and $g'' = gg'$ is in G. Associativity follows from the corresponding property in $G \times H$; the identity is (e_G,e_H) and the inverse of (g,e_H) is (g^{-1},e_H). We assert that K is isomorphic to G under the one to one mapping

$$\phi: \quad (g,e_H) \leftrightarrow g$$

since

$$\phi((g,e_H)(g',e_H)) = \phi((gg',e_H)) = gg' = \phi((g,e_H))\phi((g',e_H)).$$

Similarly, the totality of elements of the form (e_G,h), where h is arbitrary in H, form a subgroup J of $G \times H$ which is isomorphic to H.

The group K of the above theorem can also be written as

$$K = G \times I_H,$$

where I_H is the identity subgroup of H, that is, the group consisting of the single element $\{e_H\}$. Hence the above theorem could be written

$$G \times I_H \approx G.$$

It is sometimes convenient to "identify $G \times I_H$ with G" and write $G \times I_H = G$ (cf. page 24). That is, we write every element of the form (g,e_H) simply as g. For example, the equation

$$(g,h)(g',e_H) = (gg',h)$$

in $G \times H$ would become simply

$$(g,h)g' = (gg',h).$$

Similar remarks apply to $I_G \times H$ which is the group J introduced in the above theorem, I_G being the identity subgroup of G.

Another not quite so elementary theorem concerning factor groups of direct products is :

$I_G = \{ e_G \}$ $I_H = \{ e_H \}$

Theorem 18.   Let G and H be two abstract groups, $G \times H$ their direct product, and I_G and I_H the identity subgroups of G and H, respectively.   Then the factor group of $G \times H$ by $G \times I_H$ is isomorphic to $I_G \times H$, and the factor group of $G \times H$ by $I_G \times H$ is isomorphic to $G \times I_H$.

Proof: We shall prove only the first isomorphism, the proof of the second being identical.   First we shall show that the subgroup $G \times I_H$ of $G \times H$ is a *normal* subgroup.   That is, we shall show that

$$(g,h)^{-1}(g',e_H)(g,h)$$

is an element in $G \times I_H$, where g and g' are arbitrary elements in G, and h is arbitrary in H.   This is readily done :

$$(g,h)^{-1}(g',e_H)(g,h) = (g^{-1},h^{-1})(g',e_H)(g,h) = (g^{-1}g'g,h^{-1}e_Hh)$$
$$= (g'',e_H)$$

and $g'' = g^{-1}g'g$ is an element in G, since G is closed.

Since $G \times I_H$ is a normal subgroup of $G \times H$, the factor group

$$(G \times H)/(G \times I_H)$$

is a group.

Every element of the form (e_G,h), that is, every element in $I_G \times H$, appears in one of the cosets

$$(G \times I_H)(g,h)$$

[elements of the factor group $(G \times H)/(G \times I_H)$], since (g^{-1},e_H) is an element of $G \times I_H$ and

$$(g^{-1},e_H)(g,h) = (e_G,h).$$

We establish a mapping of the elements in $I_G \times H$ and the cosets in $(G \times H)/(G \times I_H)$ by associating with every element (e_G,h) in $I_G \times H$ the coset $(G \times I_H)(g,h)$ of $(G \times H)/(G \times I_H)$ in which (e_G,h) appears.   We assert that the mapping

$$\phi: \quad (G \times I_H)(g,h) \leftrightarrow (e_G,h)$$

coset of factor group

is a one to one mapping.

Since distinct cosets contain distinct elements, each (e_G,h) is mapped on only one coset,

$$(e_G,h) \rightarrow (G \times I_H)(g,h).$$

Conversely, suppose (e_G,h) and (e_G,h') are mapped onto the same coset. Then both (e_G,h) and (e_G,h') must be elements of this coset, and hence

$$(e_G,h')(e_G,h)^{-1}$$

must be an element of $G \times I_H$.   But

$$(e_G,h')(e_G,h)^{-1} = (e_G,h')(e_G,h^{-1}) = (e_G,h'h^{-1})$$

and hence

$$h'h^{-1} = e_H \quad \text{or} \quad h' = h$$

since $(e_G,h'h^{-1})$ is in $G \times I_H$.   Therefore the mapping

$$\phi: \qquad (G \times I_H)(g,h) \leftrightarrow (e_G,h)$$

is a one to one mapping.   To show that ϕ is an isomorphism,

$$\phi([(G \times I_H)(g,h)][(G \times I_H)(g',h')]) = \phi((G \times I_H)(gg',hh')) = (e_G,hh')$$
$$= (e_G,h)(e_G,h')$$
$$= \phi((G \times I_H)(g,h))\phi((G \times I_H)(g',h')).$$

Some immediate properties of direct products are:

Theorem 19. (i) $G \times I_H$ and $I_G \times H$ have only the identity element in common.

(ii) Every element of $G \times I_H$ commutes with every element of $I_G \times H$,

(iii) Every element of $G \times H$ can be uniquely expressed as the product of an element in $G \times I_H$ by an element in $I_G \times H$.

Proof of (i): The elements of $G \times I_H$ are of the form (g,e_H) and those of $I_G \times H$ are of the form (e_G,h).   Hence if (g,e_H) is to be in $I_G \times H$ we must have $g = e_G$.

Proof of (ii): $(g,e_H)(e_G,h) = (g,h) = (e_G,h)(g,e_H)$.

Proof of (iii): If (g,h) is an element of $G \times H$, then

$$(g,h) = (g,e_H)(e_G,h).$$

Hence there is at least one representation.   Suppose

$$(g,h) = (g,e_H)(e_G,h)$$

and

$$(g,h) = (g',e_H)(e_G,h').$$

Then
$$(g,e_H)(e_G,h) = (g,h) = (g',h') = (g',e_H)(e_G,h')$$

and $g = g'$, $h = h'$. Therefore there is at most one representation.

The above theorem completely characterizes the direct product in the following sense.

Theorem 20. Let G be a group and H and K subgroups of G with the following properties:

(i) Every element of H commutes with every element of K.

(ii) Every element g of G can be uniquely expressed in the form $g = hk$, where h is an element in H, and k is an element in K.

Then:

(a) H and K have only the identity in common.

(b) G is isomorphic to the direct product of H by K, $G \approx H \times K$.

Proof of (a): Since H and K are subgroups of G, the identity e of G must be in both H and K. Suppose H and K contain the common element $x \neq e$. Then H and K must also both contain x^{-1} since the intersection of two subgroups of a group is also a subgroup. Now by (ii), every element g in G can be expressed uniquely in the form

$$g = hk \tag{1.19}$$

where h is in H and k is in K. But g also equals

$$(hx)(x^{-1}k),$$

where hx is in H and $x^{-1}k$ is in K. This contradicts the unique representation of Equation 1.19.

Proof of (b): Let g be an arbitrary element in G. Then by (ii)

$$g = hk$$

uniquely where h is in H and k is in K. Consider the correspondence

$$\phi: \quad g = hk \leftrightarrow (h,k),$$

where (h,k) is an element of $H \times K$. Clearly ϕ is a one to one mapping of G onto $H \times K$. To show that this mapping is an isomorphism, let $g_1 = h_1 k_1$ and $g_2 = h_2 k_2$. Then

$$\phi(g_1 g_2) = \phi(h_1 k_1 h_2 k_2) = \phi(h_1 h_2 k_1 k_2) = (h_1 h_2, k_1 k_2)$$
$$= (h_1, k_1)(h_2, k_2) = \phi(g_1)\phi(g_2).$$

The converse of Theorem 20 is also true, that is:

Theorem 21. If H and K are subgroups of a group G and the direct product of H by K is isomorphic to G, $H \times K \approx G$, then:

(i) Every element of H commutes with every element of K.
(ii) Every element of G can be uniquely expressed in the form $g = hk$, where h is an element in H and k is an element in K.
(iii) H and K have only the identity in common.

Proof: By Theorem 19, the three properties of H and K appearing in the statement of Theorem 21 are true for $H \times I_K$ and $I_H \times K$ with respect to the group $H \times K$. Hence by the isomorphisms of Theorem 17, namely, $H \approx H \times I_K$ and $K \approx I_H \times K$, and the isomorphism $G \approx H \times K$ in the hypothesis of Theorem 21; these properties are also true for H and K with respect to the group G.

As an example of the previous theorems, consider a cyclic group G of order six with generator a,

$$G: \qquad \{e, a, a^2, a^3, a^4, a^5\}.$$

Two subgroups H and K of G are

$$H: \qquad \{e, a^2, a^4\}$$
$$K: \qquad \{e, a^3\}.$$

We assert that the above subgroups H and K satisfy conditions (i) and (ii) of Theorem 20. Clearly every element of H commutes with every element of K, since G is abelian. And from the equations

$$e = ee$$
$$a = a^4 a^3$$
$$a^2 = a^2 e$$
$$a^3 = ea^3$$
$$a^4 = a^4 e$$
$$a^5 = a^2 a^3$$

we have every element of G expressed uniquely in the form hk, where h is in H and k is in K. Hence from Theorem 20 we conclude that H and K have only the identity in common and furthermore that $G \approx H \times K$. In this concrete example we see immediately that $\{e\} = H \cap K$. The elements in the direct product $H \times K$ are

$$H \times K: \qquad \{(e,e), (e,a^3), (a^2,e), (a^2,a^3), (a^4,e), (a^4,a^3)\}$$

and under the one to one mapping,

$$e \leftrightarrow (e,e)$$
$$a \leftrightarrow (a^4,a^3)$$
$$a^2 \leftrightarrow (a^2,e)$$
$$a^3 \leftrightarrow (e,a^3)$$
$$a^4 \leftrightarrow (a^4,e)$$
$$a^5 \leftrightarrow (a^2,a^3)$$

G and $H \times K$ are isomorphic.

Referring to Theorem 17, we see that the elements of $H \times I_K$ are

$$H \times I_K: \qquad \{(e,e), (a^2,e), (a^4,e)\} \qquad\qquad (1.20)$$

and that

$$H \approx H \times I_K$$

under the one to one mapping

$$e \leftrightarrow (e,e)$$
$$a^2 \leftrightarrow (a^2,e)$$
$$a^4 \leftrightarrow (a^4,e).$$

Similarly the elements of $I_H \times K$ are

$$I_H \times K: \qquad \{(e,e), (e,a^3)\} \qquad\qquad (1.21)$$

and $I_H \times K$ is isomorphic to K under the mapping

$$e \leftrightarrow (e,e)$$
$$a^3 \leftrightarrow (e,a^3).$$

Referring to Theorem 18, the elements of the factor group $(H \times K)/(H \times I_K)$ are

$$(H \times K)/(H \times I_K): \qquad \{(H \times I_K)(e,e), (H \times I_K)(e,a^3)\}$$

and

$$(H \times K)/(H \times I_K) \approx I_H \times K$$

under the one to one mapping

$$(H \times I_K)(e,e) \leftrightarrow (e,e)$$
$$(H \times I_K)(e,a^3) \leftrightarrow (e,a^3).$$

Similarly, the elements of $(H \times K)/(I_H \times K)$ are

$$(H \times K)/(I_H \times K): \quad \{(I_H \times K)(e,e), (I_H \times K)(a^2,e), (I_H \times K)(a^4,e)\}$$

and

$$(H \times K)/(I_H \times K) \approx H \times I_K$$

under the one to one mapping

$$(I_H \times K)(e,e) \leftrightarrow (e,e)$$
$$(I_H \times K)(a^2,e) \leftrightarrow (a^2,e)$$
$$(I_H \times K)(a^4,e) \leftrightarrow (a^4,e).$$

Referring to Theorem 19, we see from Equations 1.20 and 1.21 that $H \times I_K$ and $I_H \times K$ have only the identity in common, that every element of $H \times I_K$ commutes with every element of $I_H \times K$ and that every element in $H \times K$ can be uniquely expressed as the product of an element in $H \times I_K$ by an element in $I_H \times K$, viz:

$$(e,e) = (e,e)(e,e)$$
$$(e,a^3) = (e,e)(e,a^3)$$
$$(a^2,e) = (a^2,e)(e,e)$$
$$(a^2,a^3) = (a^2,e)(e,a^3)$$
$$(a^4,e) = (a^4,e)(e,e)$$
$$(a^4,a^3) = (a^4,e)(e,a^3).$$

We leave the verification of Theorem 21 in this concrete instance as an exercise for the reader.

1.14. Basis Theorem for Abelian Groups

In our final section on group theory we shall consider an important theorem which gives an insight into the structure of finite abelian groups. If G is a group, and g is any element in G, then we know (cf. Section 1.5) that the totality of elements $\{e, g^{\pm 1}, g^{\pm 2}, \cdots\}$ forms a cyclic subgroup of G with generator g. If G is finite, not all the g^k are distinct. Let m be the smallest positive integer such that $g^m = e$. Then we shall call m the *order* of the element g in G. As seen in Section 1.5, g generates a cyclic group of order m.

We shall now consider arbitrary *finite abelian* groups.

Definition. Let G be a finite abelian group. The elements $a_1, a_2, \cdots$, a_s in G will be said to *generate* G if every element g in G can be written in the form

$$g = a_1^{n_1} a_2^{n_2} \cdots a_s^{n_s}.$$

If no set having fewer than s members generates G, then the set of elements $a_1, a_2, \cdots, a_s$ will be said to be a *minimal generating system*. We shall also say G is the direct product of its subgroups

$G_1, G_2, \cdots, G_s$ if G is isomorphic to this direct product. By Theorem 21 every element of G can be expressed uniquely in the form

$$g = g_1 g_2 \cdots g_s$$

where g_i is in G_i and the isomorphism implies the one-to-one mapping

$$g_1 g_2 \cdots g_s \leftrightarrow (g_1, g_2, \cdots, g_s).$$

By the theorems of the previous section on direct products we may identify $(g_1, g_2, \cdots, g_s)$ with $g_1 g_2 \cdots g_s$ and write

$$G = G_1 \times G_2 \times \cdots \times G_s.$$

Before stating and proving our fundamental theorem we shall consider some properties of generating systems. We note first that the number of elements in a minimal generating system is unique; however, the elements themselves need not be. For example, in the cyclic group (that is, $s = 1$) of order five,

$$G: \qquad \{e, a, a^2, a^3, a^4\}$$

any element other than the identity generates G (since G is of prime order). Clearly a generates G, and, for example, a^2 also generates G:

$$(a^2)^0 = e$$
$$(a^2)^1 = a^2$$
$$(a^2)^2 = a^4$$
$$(a^2)^3 = a$$
$$(a^2)^4 = a^3.$$

As an example of a group which has a minimal generating system containing more than one element (that is, G is not cyclic, $s > 1$), consider the group G' of order four whose multiplication table is

	e	a	b	c
e	e	a	b	c
a	a	e	c	b
b	b	c	e	a
c	c	b	a	e

A generating system for this group is a and b, since

$$e = a^0 b^0$$
$$a = a^1 b^0$$
$$b = a^0 b^1$$
$$c = a^1 b^1.$$

This generating system is also a *minimal* generating system since no single element generates G' (the order of G' being four and the order of every element in G' being one or two).

We now state our fundamental theorem for finite abelian groups.

Theorem 22. If G is a finite abelian group, it can be expressed as the direct product of s cyclic subgroups of G:

$$G_1, G_2, \cdots, G_s,$$

where the order of G_i divides the order of G_{i+1} and s is the number of elements in a minimal generating system. (The set of elements $a_1, a_2, \cdots, a_s$ which generates $G_1, G_2, \cdots, G_s$, respectively, is called a *basis* for G.)

Proof: The proof will be by complete induction on the number of elements s in a minimal generating system. Suppose $s = 1$. Then G is cyclic and the theorem is trivial. We shall now assume that the theorem has been proved for $s = 1, 2, \cdots, k - 1$. Let, then, G be a finite abelian group with k elements in its minimal generating system.

Suppose the elements

$$a_1, a_2, \cdots, a_k$$

of orders $\alpha_1, \alpha_2, \cdots, \alpha_k$, respectively, form a minimal generating system for G. Then there exist relations of the form

$$e = a_1^{m_1} a_2^{m_2} \cdots a_k^{m_k}; \tag{1.22}$$

for example, let each m_i be a multiple of α_i. Now for all possible minimal generating systems and all relations of the form of Equation 1.22, choose the one in which the smallest positive exponent, say m_1, occurs. We assert that m_1 must divide m_j, $j = 2, 3, \cdots, k$. For suppose m_1 does not divide, say m_2. Then

$$m_2 = q_1 m_1 + r_1, \qquad 0 < r_1 < m_1.$$

Thus for the generating system,

$$a_1 a_2^{q_1}, a_2, a_3, \cdots, a_k,$$

we would have the relation

$$e = (a_1 a_2^{q_1})^{m_1} a_2^{r_1} a_3^{m_3} \cdots a_k^{m_k}, \tag{1.23}$$

which contradicts the minimal character of m_1.

We conclude therefore that

$$m_j = q_j m_1, \qquad j = 2, 3, \cdots, k.$$

The system

$$b_1 = a_1 a_2^{q_2} a_3^{q_3} \cdots a_k^{q_k}, a_2, a_3, \cdots, a_k$$

is, of course, a minimal generating system and from Equation 1.22,

$$b_1^{m_1} = e.$$

We assert that m_1 is the order of b_1. For suppose $b_1^p = e$ with $0 < p < m_1$. Then

$$b_1^p = e = a_1^p a_2^{pq_2} a_3^{pq_3} \cdots a_k^{pq_k}$$

which again violates the minimal character of m_1.

Now let G^* be that subgroup of G generated by $a_2, a_3, \cdots, a_k$ and let G_1 be the cyclic subgroup of order m_1 generated by b_1. We assert that every element g in G can be uniquely written in the form

$$g = b_1^{t_1} a^*$$

where $0 \le t_1 < m_1$ and $a^* = a_2^{t_2} a_3^{t_3} \cdots a_k^{t_k}$ is in G^*. For if we could also write g as $b_1^{u_1} a^{**}$ with $0 \le u_1 < m_1$ and a^{**} in G^*, then

$$e = b_1^{t_1 - u_1} a^* (a^{**})^{-1} = b_1^{u_1 - t_1} (a^*)^{-1} a^{**}$$

which implies $t_1 = u_1$ or else the minimal character of m_1 would be violated. Therefore we also have $a^* = a^{**}$. Theorem 20 then tells us that G is isomorphic to the direct product of G_1 by G^*, which we write as

$$G = G_1 \times G^*.$$

By the induction hypothesis G^* is the direct product of $k - 1$ cyclic subgroups $G_2, G_3, \cdots, G_k$ generated, say, by $b_2, b_3, \cdots, b_k$ of orders $\beta_2, \beta_3, \cdots, \beta_k$, respectively, such that β_i divides β_{i+1}, $i = 2, 3, \cdots,$ $k - 1$. Hence to complete the proof all we need show is that m_1 divides β_2. Suppose the contrary. Then

$$\beta_2 = q m_1 + v, \qquad 0 < v < m_1$$

and from the identity

$$e = b_1^{m_1} b_2^{\beta_2} b_3^{\beta_3} \cdots b_k^{\beta_k}$$

we conclude

$$e = (b_1 b_2^q)^{m_1} b_2^v b_3^{\beta_3} \cdots b_k^{\beta_k}$$

which violates the minimal character of m_1.

The above theorem can be generalized to infinite abelian groups with a *finite* number of generators. For example, the cyclic group $\{1, 2^{\pm 1}, 2^{\pm 2}, \cdots\}$ is an infinite abelian group with a single generator, namely, 2.

EXERCISES

1.1. Show that the set of even integers forms an additive group, while the set of odd integers does not form a group under addition.

1.2. Let n be a positive integer. Show that the n roots of the equation $x^n - 1 = 0$ form a multiplicative group of order n.

1.3. Prove that the totality of real valued functions $f(x)$ of the real variable x defined and continuous on the unit interval $[0, 1]$ forms a group under the binary operation of addition.

1.4. (a) Let p be a prime number. If two integers a and b are assumed to be identical if their difference is divisible by p, prove that the p numbers

$$\{0, 1, 2 \cdots, p - 1\}$$

form an additive group.

(b) Under the hypothesis of (a) above, show that the $p - 1$ numbers

$$\{1, 2, 3, \cdots, p - 1\}$$

form a multiplicative group.

1.5. Show by example that "exponentiation" is not an associative operation.

1.6. Construct all abstract groups of order four.

1.7. Let G be a group of prime order. Prove that any element other than the identity generates G.

1.8. Prove that if for every element a in a group G, $a^2 = e$, then G is an abelian group.

1.9. Let V be the totality of ordered n-tuples of real numbers: $\alpha = \{\alpha_1, \alpha_2, \cdots, \alpha_n\}$, $\beta = \{\beta_1, \beta_2, \cdots, \beta_n\}$. If addition of n-tuples is defined as

$$\alpha + \beta = \{\alpha_1 + \beta_1, \alpha_2 + \beta_2, \cdots, \alpha_n + \beta_n\},$$

show that V is an abelian group.

1.10. Prove in detail that the right axioms are equivalent to the left axioms.

1.11. Let G be a set closed with respect to a binary operation $*$ which is associative. If there exists a *left* identity and a *right* inverse for every element of G, show by example that G is not necessarily a group.

1.12. Prove that every noncommutative group contains proper subgroups.

1.13. Let G be the additive group of all real valued functions $f(x)$ of the real variable x which are continuous on the unit interval $[0,1]$. Show that the totality of differentiable functions on $[0,1]$ forms a subgroup of G.

1.14. Let V be the group of ordered n-tuples of real numbers (cf. Exercise 1.9). If V_k consists of all elements α in V such that $\alpha_k \equiv 0$, prove that V_k is a subgroup of V.

1.15. Consider the abelian group G of order twelve consisting of the elements

$$e, a, a^2, a^3, b, b^2, \alpha, \beta, \xi, \delta, \epsilon, \zeta$$

where $a^4 = e$, $b^3 = e$, $\alpha = ab$, $\beta = ab^2$, $\xi = a^2b$, $\delta = a^2b^2$, $\epsilon = a^3b$, $\zeta = a^3b^2$. Construct the multiplication table for G and determine all subgroups of G. Prove that G is cyclic and determine which element or elements generate G.

1.16. Prove that the set $\mathfrak{A}_n$ of all even permutations is a subgroup of the symmetric group.

1.17. Determine all subgroups of the symmetric group $\mathfrak{S}_4$.

1.18. Prove that the group of rotations of a regular tetrahedron into itself is the alternating group on four symbols.

1.19. If H and K are subgroups of a group G, prove that the totality of elements common to both H and K is also a subgroup of G.

1.20. If H and K are subgroups of a group G show that HK is a subgroup of G if and only if $HK = KH$.

1.21. If G is a finite group, prove that if a subset H of G has the property that ab is in H whenever a and b are in H, then H is a subgroup of G.

1.22. If H is a subgroup of a group G, prove that the totality of elements k which have the property that

$$k^{-1}Hk = H$$

forms a subgroup K of G.

1.23. Let G be a group and g a fixed element in G. The set N_g of all elements in G which commute with g is called the *normalizer* of g. Prove that N_g is a subgroup of G.

1.24. Prove that every subgroup of a (not necessarily finite) cyclic group is cyclic.

1.25. Prove that the alternating group $\mathfrak{A}_n$ is a normal subgroup of the symmetric group $\mathfrak{S}_n$.

1.26. Let G be a group, H and K subgroups of G with K invariant. Prove that HK is a subgroup of G.

1.27. If H and K are normal subgroups of a group G, prove that the totality of elements common to both H and K forms a normal subgroup of G.

1.28. If H and K are normal subgroups of a group G, prove that HK is a normal subgroup of G.

1.29. Let $\mathfrak{S}_3$ be the symmetric group on three objects. Determine all normal subgroups of $\mathfrak{S}_3$.

1.30. Let G be the group of rigid motions in the plane. Show that the translations form a normal subgroup of G.

1.31. Let G be a group. The set C of all elements which commute with every element of G is called the *center* of G. Prove that C is a normal subgroup of G.

1.32. Let G be a group. Consider all elements of form $xyx^{-1}y^{-1}$ where x and y are in G. Let H be the smallest subgroup containing all these elements. Prove that H is a normal subgroup of G.

1.33. Let G be a cyclic group of order 30 with generator a. Determine all factor groups of G.

1.34. Determine all factor groups of Z, M (the group of the four fourth roots of unity), and $\mathfrak{S}_3$.

1.35. Prove that the factor group G/H of Exercise 1.32 is abelian.

1.36. Prove that the totality of even integers is isomorphic to the totality of integers under addition.

1.37. If G and G' are two abstract groups of the same prime order p, prove that they are isomorphic.

1.38. Construct at least two distinct homomorphisms of V into V_k. (Cf. Exercise 1.14.)

1.39. Verify the Jordan-Hölder theorem for a cyclic group of order 60 with generator a.

1.40. Show that if G is a cyclic group of order 2^n, then there exists only one composition series.

1.41. Discuss the Jordan-Hölder theorem for the case of a finite group of order pq, where p and q are prime numbers.

1.42. Let G and H be the two groups defined in Exercise 1.4. Form the multiplication table for the direct product $G \times H$. (Use $p = 5$.)

1.43. In the example given in the text of a direct product $Z \times M$ (cf. Section 1.13) show that

$$Z \approx Z \times \{1\}$$
$$M \approx \{0\} \times M.$$

Discuss the direct product $M \times Z$.

1.44. Let G and H be cyclic groups of orders p and q, respectively, with the same generator a. Construct $G \times H$, $G \times I_H$, $I_G \times H$, $(G \times H)/(G \times I_H)$, $(G \times H)/(I_G \times H)$.

1.45. Let G be a cyclic group of order 24. Determine all pairs of subgroups H and K such that G is isomorphic to the direct product of H by K.

1.46. Let G be a cyclic group of order twelve, H and K subgroups of G of orders three and four, respectively. Verify Theorems 17, 18, 19, 20, and 21 for G.

1.47. Let G be a cyclic group of order pq, where p and q are distinct prime numbers. Prove that G is the direct product of two groups H and K of orders p and q, respectively.

1.48. Generalize the theorems of Section 1.13 on direct products to the direct product of three or more groups. For example, if A, B, and C are three groups, then the elements of $A \times B \times C$ will be triplets (a,b,c) where a is in A, b is in B, and c is in C. Define group multiplication in $A \times B \times C$. Investigate the subgroups $A \times B \times I_C$, $A \times I_B \times C$, $I_A \times B \times C$, $A \times I_B \times I_C$, etc. as well as the factor groups, for example, $(A \times B \times C)/(A \times B \times I_C)$.

1.49. Let G be an abelian group of order eight containing the element a of order four, the element b of order two, and elements $\alpha = ab$, $\beta = a^2b$, $\gamma = a^3b$. Determine the multiplication table of G, all subgroups of G and the number of elements in a minimal generating system.

1.50. Let G be an abelian group of order twelve which contains the element a of order four, the element b of order three; and the products $a^n b^m$

are defined as $\alpha = ab$, $\beta = ab^2$, $\gamma = a^2b$, $\delta = a^2b^2$, $\epsilon = a^3b$, $\eta = a^3b^2$. Prove that G is isomorphic to the direct product of H by K, where H is the cyclic subgroup generated by a, and K is the cyclic subgroup generated by b.   Also prove that G is cyclic.

1.51. Prove that every abelian group of order 15 is cyclic.

1.52. Let $G_1, G_2, \cdots, G_n$ be abstract groups of distinct prime orders.   Prove that $G = G_1 \times G_2 \times \cdots \times G_n$ is cyclic.

CHAPTER 2

Rings and Ideals

2.1 Rings

In our study of groups we considered sets which were closed with respect to a *single* binary operation. Some of the examples, we considered, for example, Z, the set of all integers, also had the property of being closed with respect to *both* addition and multiplication. From a consideration of such examples and other factors, we are invited to define a system of double composition which we shall call a *ring*. It will appear that the definition we are about to make yields many fruitful results.

Definition. A *ring R* is an additive abelian group with the additional properties:

1. The group R is closed with respect to a second binary operation designated "multiplication."
2. Multiplication is associative. That is,

$$(ab)c = a(bc)$$

for all elements a, b, c in R.

3. Multiplication is distributive with respect to addition on both the left and the right. That is,

$$a(b + c) = ab + ac$$
$$(b + c)a = ba + ca$$

for all elements a, b, c in R.

We saw in the previous chapter that the set Z,

$$Z: \quad \{0, \pm 1, \pm 2, \cdots\}$$

was an additive abelian group. Clearly Z is closed with respect to ordinary multiplication; and furthermore this multiplication satisfies

54

the associativity and distributivity conditions of Axioms 2 and 3 above. Hence Z is a ring under the operations of ordinary addition and multiplication.

The set of all real-valued functions of a single real variable x defined on the unit interval also forms a ring with respect to the operations of ordinary addition and multiplication. The totality of complex numbers likewise forms a ring with respect to these two binary operations.

As another example, consider the additive group G of order three where addition is "addition modulo 3" (cf. Section 1.4),

$$G: \qquad \{0, 1, 2\}.$$

There is no possibility of defining ordinary multiplication in G (in an attempt to make it a ring) since, for example, $2 \times 2 = 4$ and 4 is not a member of G. However, let us define a second binary operation in G called "multiplication modulo 3," written $\times_3$. (Cf. Exercise 1.4.) By this we mean multiply two numbers together and cast out multiples of 3 so that the remainder is 0, 1, or 2. For example, in G,

$$2 \times_3 2 = 1$$

and G becomes closed with respect to this second binary operation, $\times_3$. The remaining axioms are clearly satisfied, and hence G is a ring with respect to addition modulo 3 and multiplication modulo 3.

Another example, this time from the field of analysis, is furnished by the class of functions $\mathfrak{L}$ which are absolutely integrable. That is, let $\mathfrak{L}$ consist of all complex valued functions $f(t)$ of the real variable t such that

$$\int_{-\infty}^{\infty} |f(t)| dt < \infty.$$

We shall show that $\mathfrak{L}$ is a ring with respect to suitable binary operations. First we shall show that $\mathfrak{L}$ is an additive abelian group with respect to ordinary addition. Suppose $f(t)$ and $g(t)$ are in $\mathfrak{L}$. Then

$$\int_{-\infty}^{\infty} |f(t)| \, dt \quad \text{and} \quad \int_{-\infty}^{\infty} |g(t)| \, dt$$

are both finite. Now

$$\int_{-\infty}^{\infty} |f(t)+g(t)| \, dt \leq \int_{-\infty}^{\infty} [|f(t)| + |g(t)|] \, dt$$

$$= \int_{-\infty}^{\infty} |f(t)| \, dt + \int_{-\infty}^{\infty} |g(t)| \, dt$$

which is also finite. Hence $\mathfrak{L}$ is closed with respect to addition. Associativity is true from the corresponding property of complex numbers. The identity is the zero function, 0,

$$f(t) + 0 = 0 + f(t) = f(t)$$

and the inverse of $f(t)$ is $-f(t)$ since

$$f(t) + [-f(t)] = 0.$$

Clearly $-f(t)$ is in $\mathfrak{L}$ since $|f(t)| = |-f(t)|$.

To show that $\mathfrak{L}$ is a ring we must now define a second binary operation and show that $\mathfrak{L}$ is closed with respect to this operation. We may certainly define ordinary multiplication in $\mathfrak{L}$,

$$h(t) = f(t)g(t).$$

However, $\mathfrak{L}$ is *not* closed with respect to this operation. Example: Let

$$f(t) = g(t) = \frac{1}{\sqrt{t}}, \qquad 0 < t \leq 1$$

$$f(t) = g(t) = 0, \qquad \text{otherwise.}$$

(2.1)

Then

$$\int_{-\infty}^{\infty} |f(t)| \, dt = \int_{-\infty}^{\infty} |g(t)| \, dt = \int_{0}^{1} \frac{dt}{\sqrt{t}} = 2$$

and $f(t)$ and $g(t)$ are in $\mathfrak{L}$. But

$$\int_{-\infty}^{\infty} |h(t)| \, dt = \int_{-\infty}^{\infty} |f(t)g(t)| \, dt = \int_{0}^{1} \frac{dt}{t} = \infty$$

and $h(t)$ is not in $\mathfrak{L}$. Hence $\mathfrak{L}$ is not closed with respect to ordinary multiplication.

Consider now a different binary operation $*$ called *convolution*,

$$h(t) = f(t)*g(t),$$

where $f(t)*g(t)$ is defined by the equation

$$f(t)*g(t) = \int_{-\infty}^{\infty} f(t - \lambda)g(\lambda) \, d\lambda. \qquad (2.2)$$

It can be shown that if $f(t)$ and $g(t)$ are in $\mathfrak{L}$, then $h(t)$ is also in $\mathfrak{L}$. (The proof of this theorem makes use of Fubini's theorem and will be omitted. Cf. Bochner and Chandrasekharan, *Fourier Transforms*, Princeton University Press, 1949, page 6.) However, let us at least show that $h(t)$ is in $\mathfrak{L}$ if $f(t)$ and $g(t)$ are defined as in Equation 2.1.   In this special case we have

$$h(t) = \int_{-\infty}^{\infty} f(t - \lambda) g(\lambda)\, d\lambda = \int_0^t \frac{1}{\sqrt{t - \lambda}} \frac{1}{\sqrt{\lambda}}\, d\lambda, \qquad 0 < t \leq 1$$
$$= 0, \qquad\qquad\qquad \text{otherwise.}$$

Performing the indicated integration, we find

$$h(t) = \pi, \qquad 0 < t \leq 1$$
$$h(t) = 0, \qquad \text{otherwise}$$

and clearly

$$\int_{-\infty}^{\infty} |h(t)|\, dt = \int_0^1 \pi\, dt = \pi$$

is finite.

The remaining axioms are easy to verify and we conclude therefore that $\mathfrak{L}$ is a ring with respect to ordinary addition $+$ and convolution $*$.

The "multiplication" appearing in the definition of a ring and in the above examples is "ring multiplication."   As we have seen above, ring multiplication is not necessarily the ordinary multiplication of numbers.   We note that a ring is not necessarily a multiplicative group since no identity or inverses have been postulated.   Also, commutativity of multiplication has not been assumed.   We are thus led to make the following definitions.

Definition.   (i) An element e of a ring R is called its *unity* element if $ea = ae = a$ for every ring element a.

(ii) If the nonzero elements of a ring R form a multiplicative group, (that is, R has a unity element and every element except the additive group identity has an inverse), then we shall call the ring a *sfield* or a *skew field* or a *division ring* or a *quasi-field*.

(iii) A ring is called *commutative* if $ab = ba$ for all a, b in R.

(iv) A commutative sfield is called a *field*.

Since a ring R is an additive abelian group we shall, in the future, consistently write 0 for the *identity element* of the group and use e (or 1) for the *unity element* of the ring (if R *has* a unity element).

The identity element 0 of the additive group of an abstract ring has many properties analogous to those of the real number zero.   For example, if R is a ring and 0 is the identity element of the group, then

$$0a = a0 = 0$$

for all a in R.

Proof: From Axiom 3 of the definition of a ring,

$$ab = a(0 + b) = a0 + ab.$$

Since R is an additive group

$$a0 = a0 + 0 = a0 + ab - (ab) = ab - (ab) = 0.$$

A similar argument establishes the fact that $0a = 0$.

We can also show that $(-a)b = a(-b) = -(ab)$ and $(-a)(-b) = ab.$ For

$$0 = 0b = (a - a)b = ab + (-a)b$$

and $(-a)b$ is the additive inverse of ab, namely $-(ab)$. Similarly we show that $a(-b) = -(ab)$. Finally,

$$0 = 0(-b) = (a - a)(-b) = a(-b) + (-a)(-b) = -ab + (-a)(-b)$$

which implies that $ab = (-a)(-b)$.

From (i) of the above definition we see that if R has a unity element e, it is unique. (Cf. page 5 of Chapter 1.) For suppose e' is any other unity element. Then $e = ee' = e'$.

If a ring R has a unity element, we say "R is a ring with unity element" or "R is a ring with unity." Frequently "1" is used in place of e. It will be clear from the context whether the "1" we are using is the number one or the unity element of the ring.

An example of a ring with a unity element is Z. Here the unity element is 1, since

$$1 \cdot n = n \cdot 1 = n$$

for all integers n in Z. The ring Z is also commutative since $nm = mn$ is an elementary property of integers. Hence we may say Z is a *commutative ring with a unity element.*

An example of a ring which does *not* have a unity element is furnished by the set of all even integers N:

$$N: \quad \{0, \pm 2, \pm 4, \cdots\}.$$

Clearly N is an additive abelian group, closed with respect to multiplication, associative, and distributive. Yet there is no element e in N such that

$$en = ne = n$$

for all even integers n in N.

The ring $\mathfrak{L}$ under the operations of addition and convolution also lacks a unity element. For if a unity element $\delta(t)$ existed, then

$$\delta(t){*}f(t) = f(t){*}\delta(t) = f(t)$$

and from Equation 2.2 we would conclude that

$$f(t) = \int_{-\infty}^{\infty} f(t-\lambda)\delta(\lambda)\,d\lambda = \int_{-\infty}^{\infty} \delta(t-\lambda)f(\lambda)\,d\lambda.$$

The only "function" having this reproducing property is the Dirac delta function, $\delta(t)$.

An interesting example of a ring with a unity element is the set of integers

$$R: \quad \{0, 2, 4, 6, 8\}$$

which form a ring under the binary operations of addition and multiplication modulo ten. At first appearance it seems that R does not have a unity element. Closer inspection, however, shows that 6 is the unity since

$$0 \times_{10} 6 = 0$$
$$2 \times_{10} 6 = 2$$
$$4 \times_{10} 6 = 4$$
$$6 \times_{10} 6 = 6$$
$$8 \times_{10} 6 = 8.$$

The reader who is familiar with the elements of matrix theory can easily verify that all square two-by-two matrices form a ring with respect to the binary operations of matrix addition and multiplication. This ring has a unity element but is not commutative.

An example of a field is the set of all rational numbers. Clearly they form a module. If $a \neq 0$, then a^{-1} exists and is a rational number. Hence the nonzero elements form a multiplicative group with unity element the number one. The other axioms are trivial to verify.

2.2 Homomorphism and Isomorphism

In Section 1.9 we defined isomorphism and homomorphism for groups. We now define these concepts for the case of rings.

Definition. Let R be a ring under the binary operations $+$ and $\times$ and let $\bar{R}$ be a ring under the operations $*$ and $\circ$. Let ϕ be a mapping of R into $\bar{R}$

$$\phi: \quad R \to \bar{R}.$$

Then ϕ is said to be a *homomorphism* if

$$\phi(a + b) = \phi(a) * \phi(b)$$
$$\phi(a \times b) = \phi(a) \circ \phi(b)$$

for all a, b in R. Suppose further that ϕ is a one to one mapping of

R onto $\bar{R}$. Then we call ϕ an *isomorphism*. We say that R and $\bar{R}$ are *isomorphic* (written $R \approx \bar{R}$) if there exists an isomorphism mapping R onto $\bar{R}$.

We shall use this definition throughout the remainder of this book. In particular we shall prove for rings theorems analogous to those of Section 1.10, which were proved for groups. Before proving any theorems about homomorphisms and isomorphisms, however, we shall construct several examples.

A. Let R be a ring. A subset S of R which is also a ring with respect to the binary operations defined in R is called a *subring* of R. The subset of R consisting of the group identity 0 of R alone, namely $\{0\}$, is a subring of R. Clearly $\{0\}$ is closed with respect to addition and multiplication since $0 + 0 = 0$ and $0 \cdot 0 = 0$. The other axioms are also trivial to verify. We assert that the mapping ϕ,

$$\phi: \qquad R \to \{0\}$$

which takes every element in R into 0 is a homomorphism. For,

$$\phi(a + b) = 0 = 0 + 0 = \phi(a) + \phi(b) \tag{2.3}$$

and

$$\phi(ab) = 0 = 0 \cdot 0 = \phi(a)\phi(b). \tag{2.4}$$

B. Let Z be the ring of integers and N the ring of even integers. Clearly N is a subring of Z. We have seen earlier that the one to one mapping

$$\phi: \qquad n \leftrightarrow 2n$$

is an isomorphism. That is, the sets N and Z are isomorphic *considered as additive abelian groups*. However, with respect to ordinary addition and multiplication, ϕ is no longer an isomorphism or even a homomorphism. For example,

$$\phi(3 \cdot 4) \neq \phi(3)\phi(4) = 6 \cdot 8 = 48,$$

while

$$\phi(12) = 24.$$

Clearly $48 \neq 24$ in N and ϕ is not an isomorphism. In brief, then, Z and N *are* isomorphic as groups but are *not* isomorphic considered as rings.

However, let us define in N a binary operation $*$ (in place of multiplication) defined by the equation

$$\alpha * \beta = \frac{\alpha \cdot \beta}{2}$$

where $\alpha \cdot \beta$ is ordinary multiplication of the integers α and β. Since

α and β are even, so is $(\alpha \cdot \beta)/2$ and N is closed with respect to $*$. We easily see that N is a ring under the binary operations of $+$ and $*$, but is no longer a subring of Z. We assert that Z and N are isomorphic under the one to one mapping.

$$\psi: \qquad n \leftrightarrow 2n,$$

for

$$\psi(n)*\psi(m) = (2n)*(2m) = 2nm = \psi(nm). \qquad (2.5)$$

Our first theorem on homomorphisms is the analog of Theorem 9 of Section 1.9 of Chapter 1 for groups. If R and $\bar{R}$ are rings and ϕ is a homomorphism mapping R onto $\bar{R}$, then $\bar{R}$ is called a *homomorphic image* of R. We then have the theorem,

Theorem 1. Let ϕ be a homomorphic mapping of R into $\bar{R}$. Let $\bar{S}$ be the homomorphic image of R in $\bar{R}$. Then $\bar{S}$ is a subring of $\bar{R}$.

Proof: Since ϕ is a homomorphism of the additive group of R, $\bar{S}$ is a subgroup of the additive group of $\bar{R}$. Furthermore, if a and b are the preimages in R of any two elements $\bar{a}$ and $\bar{b}$ (respectively) in $\bar{S}$, then

$$\phi(ab) = \phi(a)\phi(b) = \bar{a}\bar{b}$$

is in $\bar{S}$ and $\bar{S}$ is closed under multiplication. Thus $\bar{S}$ is a subring of $\bar{R}$.

We saw earlier that a ring does not necessarily have a unity element (for example, the ring of even integers). This is sometimes an inconvenient restriction. We shall show in the next theorem that any ring can be imbedded in a ring that *does* have a unity element.

Theorem 2. Any ring R without a unity element can be imbedded in a ring which does have one.

Proof: Let Z be the ring of integers and $R \times Z$ the "Cartesian product" of R by Z. The elements of $R \times Z$ will be all pairs of the form (a,m), where a is in R and m is an integer in Z. We shall show that when suitable binary operations have been defined in $R \times Z$, it becomes a ring with a unity element containing a subring isomorphic to R.

If (a,m) and (b,n) are two elements in $R \times Z$, we define addition in $R \times Z$ by the equation

$$(a,m) + (b,n) = (a + b, m + n) \qquad (2.6)$$

and multiplication in $R \times Z$ by the equation

$$(a,m)(b,n) = (ab + na + mb, mn). \qquad (2.7)$$

(Note that the Cartesian product is identical with the direct product if we consider only the group property of $R \times Z$.)   Before proving that $R \times Z$ is a ring, a few words must be said about the above definitions of the binary operations in $R \times Z$.   In Equation 2.6 the plus sign appearing on the left-hand side of the equation is the plus sign of $R \times Z$. The plus sign in $a + b$ is addition in R, while the plus sign in $m + n$ is addition of integers in Z.   In Equation 2.7, the plus signs are addition in R.   By the symbol na we mean

$$a + a + \cdots + a \qquad\qquad (2.8)$$

n times, where the plus signs appearing in the above equation are again the addition defined in R.   If n is a negative integer, na is interpreted as

$$(-a) + (-a) + \cdots + (-a) \qquad\qquad (2.9)$$

where $-a$ is the additive inverse of a.   By $0 \cdot a$, where 0 is the real number zero, we mean the additive identity

$$0 \qquad\qquad (2.10)$$

of R.   We see, therefore, that na is *not* n times a since n (an integer) is not necessarily in R; but simply a shorthand notation for Equations 2.8, 2.9, or 2.10, depending on whether n is positive, negative, or zero. Similar remarks apply to mb.   By the term mn in Equation 2.7 we mean ordinary multiplication of the integers m and n.

Since $a + b$ is in R and $m + n$ is in Z by the group properties of the rings R and Z, respectively, we conclude $R \times Z$ is closed with respect to "addition."   Also ab is in R since it is closed with respect to multiplication; $na = a + a + \cdots + a$ (n factors) and $mb = b + b + \cdots + b$ (m factors) are in R since R is an additive group; and finally $ab + na + mb$ is also in R, again by the group property of R.   Since mn is an integer (in Z) we conclude that $R \times Z$ is closed with respect to multiplication.

The group identity in $R \times Z$ is $(0,0)$ since

$$(a,m) + (0,0) = (a,m) = (0,0) + (a,m).$$

The proofs of the commutativity of addition, the associativity of addition and multiplication, and the distributive laws of multiplication with respect to addition will be left as an exercise for the reader.   Hence $R \times Z$ is a ring.

The ring $R \times Z$ has a unity element, namely $(0,1)$, since

$$(a,m)(0,1) = (a0 + a + m0, m \cdot 1) = (a,m).$$

In Section 2.1 we showed that $a0 = 0$ (both 0 in R).   By definition

$m0 = 0$ (both 0 again in R). And $0 + a + 0 = a$ by the group property of R. Similarly

$$(0,1)(a,m) = (a,m)$$

and $(0,1)$ is indeed the unity element of $R \times Z$.

Consider now the subset $R \times \{0\}$ of $R \times Z$ which consists of all pairs of the form $(a,0)$. We shall show that $R \times \{0\}$ is a subring of $R \times Z$. From the equations

$$(a,0) + (b,0) = (a + b, 0 + 0) = (a + b, 0) \tag{2.11}$$

and

$$(a,0)(b,0) = (ab + 0a + 0b, 0 \cdot 0) = (ab,0) \tag{2.12}$$

we see that $R \times \{0\}$ is closed with respect to both addition and multiplication. The identity $(0,0)$ of $R \times Z$ is in $R \times \{0\}$ and the additive inverse of $(a,0)$, namely $(-a, 0)$, is also in $R \times \{0\}$. The remaining ring axioms follow from the corresponding properties of $R \times Z$.

Consider the function $\phi : R \to R \times \{0\}$ defined as follows:

$$\phi(a) = (a,0).$$

It is easily seen that ϕ is a homomorphism since

$$\phi(a + b) = (a + b, 0) = (a,0) + (b,0) = \phi(a) + \phi(b)$$

and

$$\phi(ab) = (ab,0) = (a,0)(b,0) = \phi(a)\phi(b).$$

Furthermore ϕ is one to one, so that it is an isomorphism. Thus

$$R \approx R \times \{0\}.$$

If we identify R with $R \times \{0\}$ we can actually replace $R \times \{0\}$ in $R \times Z$ by R. For, consider the set P consisting of all elements belonging to $R \times Z$ *except* those of the form $(a,0)$. That is,

$$P = R \times Z - R \times \{0\}.$$

Now add to P all elements of R. Thus we have constructed a new set R^*,

$$R^* = \{R, P\}.$$

If two elements in R^* belong to P, we define addition and multiplication as in $R \times Z$. If the result is of the form $(a,0)$ (an element in $R \times \{0\}$) we replace it by a (an element in R). If two elements in R^* belong to R, we define addition and multiplication as in R. If one element is in P, say (a,n) and the other element is in R, say b, we define addition and multiplication in R^* in the expected fashion, namely,

$$(a,n) + b = (a + b, n),$$
$$(a,n)b = ab + nb.$$

Clearly $R*$ is a ring isomorphic to $R \times Z$ and R is a subring of $R*$. Thus we have succeeded in imbedding the ring R (without a unity element) in a larger ring $R*$ (with a unity).

2.3 Integral Domains

We saw in Section 2.1 that the identity element 0 of a ring R had many of the properties of the real number zero. For example, if a is an element in R, then

$$0a = a0 = 0.$$

Hereafter we shall frequently use the term "zero" when speaking of the group identity. The context will make clear whether we mean the real number zero or the group identity.

In dealing with an arbitrary ring R there may exist elements a and b in R neither of which is 0, and yet their product may be zero. Such elements are called *divisors of zero*.

Definition. A nonzero ring element a is called a *divisor of zero* if there exists an element $b \neq 0$ in the ring such that either $ab = 0$ or $ba = 0$.

As an example of such a ring, consider the totality R of all ordered pairs of real numbers (a,b). If (a,b) and (α,β) are two elements in R, we define addition and multiplication in R by the equations

$$(a,b) + (\alpha,\beta) = (a + \alpha, b + \beta)$$
$$(a,b)(\alpha,\beta) = (a\alpha, b\beta).$$

We leave as an exercise for the reader the proof of the fact that, with these definitions, R is a ring. The identity element is $(0,0)$.

The ring has divisors of zero. Example: Let $(a,0)$ and $(0,\beta)$ with $a, \beta \neq 0$ be two elements of R. Clearly neither $(a,0)$ nor $(0,\beta)$ is the identity element, yet their product

$$(a,0)(0,\beta) = (a \cdot 0, 0 \cdot \beta) = (0,0)$$

is the identity element.

If a ring R has divisors of zero, it is impossible to define a "cancellation law." That is, we cannot conclude from the equation $ab = 0$ that either a or b (or both) is zero. We are thus led to make the following definition.

Definition. An *integral domain* or *domain of integrity* is a commutative ring with a unity element which has no divisors of zero.

Some authors prefer to define integral domain without the phrase "with unity element." Hence when we say "D is an integral domain," they would say "D is an integral domain with unity element." Conversely, when they say "D is an integral domain," we would have to say "D is a commutative ring without divisors of zero." For our purposes, the above definition is the more convenient one.

An example of an integral domain is the ring of integers Z. We have seen earlier that Z is a commutative ring with a unity element. If n and m are integers, we know that the equation

$$nm = 0$$

implies either n or m (or both) is zero. Therefore Z is free of divisors of zero and hence is an integral domain.

The ring $\mathfrak{L}$ of all absolutely integrable functions is a commutative ring. However, it fails to be an integral domain since it lacks a unity element.

To show the relation of our new definitions to some of our earlier concepts, we prove several simple theorems.

Theorem 3. A field is an integral domain.

Proof: Let $\varDelta$ be a field. Let a and b be elements of $\varDelta$ such that $ab = 0$, and let $a \neq 0$. We shall show that b must be zero. By definition of a field, every nonzero element has an inverse. Hence a^{-1} exists. Also, a field has a unity element, say e. Therefore

$$b = eb = a^{-1}ab = a^{-1}0 = 0$$

and we have $b = 0$. Since $\varDelta$ is commutative, $ba = 0$ with $a \neq 0$ also implies $b = 0$. Since a field is a commutative ring with a unity element and we have just shown that it has no divisors of zero, we conclude that $\varDelta$ is an integral domain.

A sfield $\varSigma$ is not a commutative ring. Hence we cannot hope to show that $\varSigma$ is an integral domain, since by hypothesis an integral domain is a commutative ring. However, we can show that it is free of divisors of zero.

Theorem 4. A sfield has no divisors of zero.

Proof: Let $\varSigma$ be a skew field. Let $ab = 0$ with a and b in $\varSigma$ and $a \neq 0$. By definition of a sfield, the nonzero elements of $\varSigma$ form a (not necessarily commutative) multiplicative group. Hence a^{-1} exists, and as in Theorem 3 we conclude that $b = 0$. Similarly if $b'a = 0$, with $a \neq 0$ we would conclude that $b' = 0$. This establishes the fact that $\varSigma$ has no divisors of zero.

In general, an integral domain is not a field. For example, the ring of integers Z is an integral domain, yet the nonzero elements do not have inverses under ordinary multiplication. However, for the case of *finite* domains of integrity, we have the following theorem.

Theorem 5. <u>An integral domain with a finite number of elements is a field.</u>

Proof: Let D be such an integral domain. We must show that the nonzero elements of D form a commutative multiplicative group. Since D is an integral domain, it is closed with respect to multiplication, multiplication is associative and commutative, and D has a unity element. Hence all we need prove is that every nonzero element in D has an inverse.

Suppose

$$e = a_1, a_2, \cdots, a_p$$

are the nonzero elements of D and suppose that some nonzero element, say a_2, does not have a multiplicative inverse. We shall show that this assumption leads to a contradiction.

Consider the p elements

$$a_2 a_j = a_{i_j}, \qquad j = 1, 2, \cdots, p. \qquad (2.13)$$

By closure the a_{i_j} are elements of D. Since D is an integral domain it has no divisors of zero and hence

$$a_{i_j} \neq 0, \qquad j = 1, 2, \cdots, p.$$

By assumption there is no element a_α such that

$$a_2 a_\alpha = e.$$

Hence there must be at least two of the a_{i_j} which are equal, say

$$a_{i_r} = a_{i_s}, \qquad r \neq s.$$

Equation 2.13 thus implies that

$$a_2 a_r = a_2 a_s.$$

By the distributive law of multiplication and the fact that $-(a_2 a_s) = a_2(-a_s)$ we have

$$a_2(a_r - a_s) = 0.$$

Now $a_r - a_s \neq 0$, and since D has no divisors of zero, we must have $a_2 = 0$. But a_2 is a nonzero element. Hence we have a contradiction and therefore a_2 must have a multiplicative inverse.

2.4 Equivalence Classes

In the next section we shall need the concepts of an *equivalence relation* and an *equivalence class*. These ideas are not restricted to ring theory alone. Hence in the present section we shall define these concepts and prove some of their elementary properties without recourse to any special properties of rings or groups.

Definition. Let S be a set. A symbol $\sim$ is called an *equivalence relation* for the set S if it has the following three properties:

(i) It is *reflexive*; that is, $a \sim a$ for all a in S.
(ii) It is *symmetric*; that is, if $a \sim b$, then $b \sim a$ for all a and b in S.
(iii) It is *transitive*; that is, if $a \sim b$ and $b \sim c$, then $a \sim c$ for elements a, b, c in S.

The statement "$a \sim b$" is read: "a stands in relation to b" or "a is equivalent to b."

A. If S is any set, then equality is an equivalence relation. It is reflexive since

$$a = a.$$

If $a = b$, then $b = a$; hence $=$ is symmetric. Finally, from $a = b$ and $b = c$ follows $a = c$. Hence equality is transitive.

B. The symbol $>$ (greater than) is *not* an equivalence relation with respect to real numbers. It is transitive, but it is neither reflexive nor symmetric.

C. Let G be an additive group and H a subgroup of G. We shall write $a \sim b$ if $a - b$ is in H. The symbol $\sim$ is an equivalence relation. First, it is symmetric, since $a - a = 0$ (the identity) is surely in H. Second, if $a - b$ is in H, then $b - a$ is in H, since $b - a$ is the inverse of $a - b$. Third, if $a - b$ is in H and $b - c$ is in H, then $(a - b) + (b - c) = a - c$ is in H, since H is closed.

D. Isomorphism is an equivalence relation. If, for example, G, H, and K are isomorphic groups, then certainly

$$G \approx G,$$

and $\approx$ is reflexive. From $G \approx H$ follows $H \approx G$, and $\approx$ is symmetric. Transitivity, that is, if $G \approx H$ and $H \approx K$ then $G \approx K$ follows from Theorem 12 of Chapter 1.

Suppose S is an arbitrary set in which an equivalence relation $\sim$ has been defined. Let K_a be the set of all elements in S which are equivalent to a. Then K_a is called an *equivalence class*.

Let S be the set of all rational numbers.   We shall say

$$\frac{p}{q} \sim \frac{r}{s}$$

if $ps = rq$, where p, q, r, s are integers in S.   One can readily verify that $\sim$ is an equivalence relation.   If p/q is a fixed element of S, then $K_{p/q}$ consists of all numbers of the form pn/qn, where n is a nonzero integer or the reciprocal of an integer α which divides both p and q. For example, $K_{4/6}$ consists of

$$\frac{2}{3}, \frac{4}{6}, \frac{6}{9}, \cdots$$

From the above example we see that $K_{2/3}$ and $K_{4/6}$ are the same equivalence class, since every element of $K_{2/3}$ is in $K_{4/6}$ and conversely. This is a property of equivalence classes in general which we prove in the following theorem.

Theorem 6.   Let S be a set in which an equivalence relation has been defined.   Let a and b be two elements in S and let K_a and K_b be the corresponding equivalence classes.   Then $a \sim b$ if and only if $K_a = K_b$.

Proof: Suppose $K_a = K_b$.   Let c be an element common to both. Then $c \sim a$ and $c \sim b$ by definition of equivalence classes.   By symmetry, $a \sim c$ and from the relations $a \sim c$, $c \sim b$ we conclude that $a \sim b$ by transitivity.

Conversely, suppose $a \sim b$.   Let c be an element in K_a.   Then $c \sim a$ and by transitivity, $c \sim b$.   Hence c is an element in K_b.   Therefore we see that every element in K_a is in K_b and we may write $K_a \subseteq K_b$. On the other hand, if d is in K_b, then $d \sim b$ and from the relations $d \sim b$, $b \sim a$ we conclude $d \sim a$ and hence d is in K_a.   Thus we have shown $K_b \subseteq K_a$.   From

$$K_a \subseteq K_b \quad \text{and} \quad K_b \subseteq K_a$$

we conclude that

$$K_a = K_b,$$

by definition of equality of sets.

We see from this theorem that if two equivalence classes have an element in common, then they are identical.   An immediate corollary to this theorem is: If a is *not* equivalent to b, then K_a and K_b have no element in common.   Also from the theorem we see that it is immaterial which element x in K_a is brought into prominence and written as a subscript on K.   That is, we could equally well write K_x as K_a since $x \sim a$ and hence $K_x \equiv K_a$.

In the example considered before the proof of Theorem 6, namely the set S of all rational numbers, we can divide all fractions into equivalence classes $K_a, K_b, \cdots$, where $a, b, \cdots$ are fractions customarily written in their lowest terms.

2.5 The Field of Quotients

We saw in Section 2.2 that a ring without unity element can be imbedded in a ring which *does* have a unity. However, we cannot hope to imbed an arbitrary ring in a field since, in general, a ring is non-commutative and may have divisors of zero. If D is a commutative ring free of divisors of zero, however, we shall show that it can be imbedded in a field Δ. This field Δ is called the "field of quotients" of D, or simply the "quotient field."

An example of this situation, which also furnishes the motivation underlying the proof of the general theorem, is given by the ring of integers Z. We have seen that Z is commutative and free of divisors of zero. Consider the Cartesian product of Z by $Z - \{0\}$, where $Z - \{0\}$ is the set of all integers in Z except the zero element. The elements of $Z \times (Z - \{0\})$ will be pairs (a,b), where a is an element in Z and b is an element in $Z - \{0\}$. We may write

$$(a,b) = \frac{a}{b}, \quad \text{by definition}$$

where a/b is simply a fraction. Since b is in $Z - \{0\}$, b can never be zero. Now let $K_{a/b}$ be the equivalence class of all rational numbers c/d which equal a/b and let Δ be the set of all equivalence classes $K_{a/b}$. Then under the usual definition of addition and multiplication of fractions, Δ becomes a field, namely, the field of rational numbers. Hence the quotient field of the integers is the field of rational numbers.

In the general case we cannot consider a/b since this expression is not defined. However, we *can* consider ordered pairs (a,b) and say (a,b) is equivalent to (c,d) if $ad = bc$. [If we are dealing with fractions, then the statement $ad = bc$ is, of course, equivalent to saying

$$\frac{a}{b} = \frac{c}{d}.$$

Cf. the example of the previous section preceding Theorem 6.] As a matter of convenience in notation we shall sometimes write (a,b) as $\frac{a}{b}$ even in an arbitrary field. That is, $\frac{a}{b} = ab^{-1} = b^{-1}a$. (Cf., for example, Section 2.14.)

Theorem 7. A commutative ring without divisors of zero can be imbedded in a field.

Proof: Let D be a commutative ring free of divisors of zero. Let (a,b) be an element of $D \times (D - \{0\})$. We shall say

$$(a,b) \sim (c,d)$$

if $ad - bc = 0$. First we shall show that $\sim$ is an equivalence relation. We shall then show that, when suitable binary operations have been defined, the totality of equivalence classes $K_{(a,b)}$ form a field Δ known as the *quotient field* of D.

The relation $\sim$ is reflexive,

$$(a,b) \sim (a,b),$$

since $ab - ba = 0$. (Note we have used the fact that D is commutative.) Suppose $(a,b) \sim (c,d)$, then $(c,d) \sim (a,b)$. For, from $ad - bc = 0$ follows $cb - da = 0$ (using the commutativity of both addition and multiplication). Hence $\sim$ is symmetric. Finally, $\sim$ is transitive. We shall show that if $(a,b) \sim (c,d)$ and $(c,d) \sim (e,f)$, then $(a,b) \sim (e,f)$. To prove this statement we must show

$$af - be = 0.$$

From the first two equivalence relations we have

$$ad = bc \tag{2.14}$$

and

$$cf = de. \tag{2.15}$$

Multiply these two equations together:

$$adcf = bcde.$$

By the commutativity of D and the distributivity of multiplication with respect to addition we may write

$$dc(af - be) = 0.$$

But D has no divisors of zero. Hence dc or $af - be$ or both must be zero.

Suppose $dc \neq 0$; then

$$af - be = 0 \tag{2.16}$$

and we have shown that $\sim$ is transitive. Suppose $dc = 0$. We shall show that even in this case $af - be$ is still zero. Since D is an integral domain,

$$dc = 0$$

implies d or c is zero. But d is an element in $D - \{0\}$ and hence $d \neq 0$. Therefore c must be zero. From Equation 2.14

$$ad = b0 = 0$$

and therefore a or d must be zero. But $d \neq 0$, hence $a = 0$. Also from Equation 2.15,

$$de = 0,$$

and since $d \neq 0$, e must be zero. Since both a and e are zero,

$$af - be = 0f - b0 = 0.$$

Therefore $\sim$ is transitive and hence an equivalence relation.

Before showing that the equivalence classes $K_{(a,b)}$ form a field $\varDelta$ we must define addition and multiplication in $\varDelta$. This we do by the following equations:

$$K_{(a,b)} + K_{(c,d)} = K_{(ad+bc,\ bd)}$$
$$K_{(a,b)}K_{(c,d)} = K_{(ac,bd)}.$$

In the above equations the results are independent of the choice of the representative element from the equivalence classes. For if $(a,b) \sim (a',b')$ and $(c,d) \sim (c',d')$, then $ab' = a'b$ and $cd' = c'd$, from which it follows that $acb'd' = bda'c'$ and therefore $(ac,bd) \sim (a'c',b'd')$. Thus since

$$K_{(a',b')}K_{(c',d')} = K_{(a'c',b'd')}$$

we conclude

$$K_{(a'c',b'd')} \equiv K_{(ac,bd)}.$$

Similarly

$$K_{(a'd'+b'c',\ b'd')} \equiv K_{(ad+bc,\ bd)}.$$

Addition and multiplication are both closed. First $ad + bc$ and ac are in D, since D is closed with respect to addition and multiplication. Since b and d are both in $D - \{0\}$, b and d are both unequal to zero. Also, since D has no divisors of zero, their product bd is not zero and hence in $D - \{0\}$. Therefore the set $\varDelta$ is closed with respect to both addition and multiplication.

To show that $\varDelta$ is a field, we must first show that it is an additive abelian group. We have seen above that it is closed. Associativity follows from the equations

$$K_{(a,b)} + [K_{(c,d)} + K_{(e,f)}] = K_{(a,b)} + K_{(cf+de,\ df)}$$
$$= K_{(adf+bcf+bde,\ bdf)}$$

and

$$[K_{(a,b)} + K_{(c,d)}] + K_{(e,f)} = K_{(ad+bc,\ bd)} + K_{(e,f)}$$
$$= K_{(adf+bcf+bde,\ bdf)}.$$

The identity is $K_{(0,b)}$, since

$$K_{(0,b)} + K_{(c,d)} = K_{(0d+bc,\ bd)} = K_{(bc,bd)} = K_{(c,d)}$$

and $(bc,bd) \sim (c,d)$.

The inverse of $K_{(a,b)}$ is $K_{(-a,\ b)}$, for

$$K_{(a,b)} + K_{(-a,\ b)} = K_{(ab-ba,\ bb)} = K_{(0,bb)} = K_{(0,b)}$$

since D is commutative and $(0,bb) \sim (0,b)$.

Hence we see that $\varDelta$ is an additive group, and $\varDelta$ is abelian since

$$K_{(a,b)} + K_{(c,d)} = K_{(ad+bc,\ bd)} = K_{(cb+da,\ db)} = K_{(c,d)} + K_{(a,b)}$$

by the commutativity and associativity of D.

Next we must show that the nonzero elements of $\varDelta$ form a commutative multiplicative group. Closure has been proved above. Associativity follows from

$$K_{(a,b)}[K_{(c,d)}K_{(e,f)}] = K_{(a,b)}K_{(ce,df)} = K_{(ace,bdf)}$$
$$= K_{(ac,bd)}K_{(e,f)} = [K_{(a,b)}K_{(c,d)}]K_{(e,f)}.$$

The unity is $K_{(a,a)}$, since

$$K_{(a,a)}K_{(b,c)} = K_{(ab,ac)} = K_{(b,c)}$$

and $(ab,ac) \sim (b,c)$.

Let $K_{(a,b)}$ be a nonzero element of $\varDelta$. This implies a is not zero and hence is an element in $D - \{0\}$. Therefore $K_{(b,a)}$ is defined. Then $K_{(b,a)}$ is the multiplicative inverse of $K_{(a,b)}$, since

$$K_{(b,a)}K_{(a,b)} = K_{(ba,ab)} = K_{(a,a)},$$

(a,a) being equivalent to (ba,ab).

The commutativity of multiplication in $\varDelta$ follows from the equation

$$K_{(a,b)}K_{(c,d)} = K_{(ac,bd)} = K_{(ca,db)} = K_{(c,d)}K_{(a,b)}.$$

To complete the proof we must show that multiplication is distributive with respect to addition. We have

$$K_{(a,b)}[K_{(c,d)} + K_{(e,f)}] = K_{(a,b)}[K_{(cf+de,\ df)}] = K_{(acf+ade,\ bdf)}$$

and

$$K_{(a,b)}K_{(c,d)} + K_{(a,b)}K_{(c,f)} = K_{(ac,bd)} + K_{(ae,bf)}$$
$$= K_{(acbf+bdae,\ bdbf)}.$$

The equivalence classes $K_{(acf+ade,\ bdf)}$ and $K_{(acbf+bdae,\ bdbf)}$ are identical since

$$(acf + ade,\ bdf) \sim (acbf + bdae,\ bdbf)$$

as can be seen from the equation

$$(acf + ade)(bdbf) - (bdf)(acbf + bdae) = 0.$$

The proof of the distributivity on the right, namely

$$[K_{(a,b)} + K_{(c,d)}]K_{(e,f)} = K_{(a,b)}K_{(e,f)} + K_{(c,d)}K_{(e,f)}$$

follows by commutativity.

The above theorem will be used in our development of field theory in the next chapter. Another associated theorem that will be left as an exercise for the reader is: If R and S are two commutative rings without divisors of zero, and R is isomorphic to S, then their quotient fields are also isomorphic.

2.6 Residue Classes

In our study of group theory we found that one of the most powerful tools available for investigating the structure of groups was the *normal subgroup*. We proved, for example, the fundamental theorem (Theorem 10 of Chapter 1) that if ϕ were a homomorphism mapping G onto $\bar{G}$, then $G/H \approx \bar{G}$, where H was the set of preimages which mapped onto the identity of $\bar{G}$. Of course H was a normal subgroup. We have defined earlier in the present chapter the concept of a *subring* of a ring. It is not surprising, therefore, that if additional restrictions are placed on a subring it becomes a set which will play the same rôle in ring theory that the normal subgroup did in group theory. This analogous set is called an *ideal*—which we define as follows:

Definition. If N is an additive subgroup of a ring R such that both ra and ar are in N for all elements a in N and all ring elements r in R, then we say N is an *ideal*. Clearly an ideal is also a subring.

If Z is the ring of integers, then the set of even integers N forms an ideal. We have seen that N is a subring. Now if α is an arbitrary integer in Z and 2β is an even integer in N, then certainly

$$\alpha(2\beta) = (2\beta)\alpha$$

is an even integer and hence in N.

In the definition of an ideal we required N to contain both ra and ar, since in general R is not commutative and hence ra and ar are not necessarily equal. Such an ideal is sometimes called a *two-sided* ideal.

If we only require ra to be in N, then N would be a *left ideal* and if we only required ar to be in N, then N would be a *right ideal*. We shall deal exclusively with two-sided ideals, or as we shall simply say, ideals.

An important homomorphism theorem analogous to the first part of Theorem 10 of Chapter 1 for groups is:

Theorem 8. Let ϕ be a homomorphism mapping the ring R onto the ring $\bar{R}$. Then the set of elements N of the preimages of the identity $\bar{0}$ of $\bar{R}$ forms an ideal in R.

Proof: Suppose a and b are in N. Then

$$\phi(a + b) = \phi(a) + \phi(b) = \bar{0} + \bar{0} = \bar{0}$$

and

$$\phi(ab) = \phi(a)\phi(b) = \bar{0} \cdot \bar{0} = \bar{0}.$$

Hence N is closed.

Associativity of addition and multiplication, commutativity of addition, and distributivity of multiplication with respect to addition follow from the corresponding properties of R, since N is a subset of R. By Theorem 10 of Chapter 1 we know that N is an additive group. Hence N is a subring of R. To show that N is an ideal, let r be an arbitrary element in R and a any element in N. Then

$$\phi(ar) = \phi(a)\phi(r) = \bar{0}\phi(r) = \bar{0}$$

and

$$\phi(ra) = \phi(r)\phi(a) = \phi(r)\bar{0} = \bar{0}.$$

(This also proves, again, the closure of N with respect to multiplication.)

In group theory we formed the factor group G/H of G by H, where H was a normal subgroup of G. The elements of G/H were *cosets*. If R is a ring and N an ideal in R, then the set of elements of the form $a + n$ where a is a fixed element in R and n ranges throughout N is called a *residue class* or a *remainder class*. Clearly $a + N$ is also a coset, since N, being an ideal, is, in particular, a subgroup. Since R is an *additive* group we write residue classes in the additive notation $a + N$ rather than the multiplicative notation aN as was more common in group theory.

If R is an arbitrary ring and N is an ideal in R, then we may form a new set whose elements are the residue classes of N in R. This set is generally written R/N and could be called a "factor ring," although this term is not prevalent in the literature. Since R is an additive *abelian* group, N is a normal subgroup and hence R/N is the factor group of R by N. We saw in Theorem 8 of Chapter 1 that R/N was a *group*. Now we shall show that R/N is a *ring*.

Theorem 9.   The set of residue classes of an ideal in a ring forms a ring.

Proof: Since the residue classes are also cosets, they are distinct. That is, if R is the ring and N is an ideal in R, then $a + N$ and $b + N$ are either identical or else have no elements in common.   Also since they are cosets, we can write $\alpha + N$ in place of $a + N$ if α is an element in $a + N$.   For if this be the case, $\alpha = a + n$, where n is in N and $\alpha + N = (a + n) + N = a + (n + N) = a + N$, since N is an additive group.   Hence we see that we can operate with any representative element of $a + N$.   (Cf. Theorem 4 of Chapter 1.)

Addition of residue classes is defined as addition of cosets.   That is, by $(a + N) + (b + N)$ we mean the totality of elements of the form $\alpha + \beta$, where α is in $a + N$ and β is in $b + N$.   Since N is a module, we have

$$(a + N) + (b + N) = (a + b) + (N + N) = (a + b) + N.$$

Multiplication of residue classes is defined as

$$(a + N)(b + N) = ab + N. \tag{2.17}$$

We must show that if $a + N = \alpha + N$ and $b + N = \beta + N$, then $ab + N = \alpha\beta + N$.   Now $a = \alpha + n_1$ and $b = \beta + n_2$ with n_1 and n_2 in N, and

$$ab = (\alpha + n_1)(\beta + n_2) = \alpha\beta + \alpha n_2 + n_1\beta + n_1 n_2 = \alpha\beta + n'.$$

Therefore $ab - \alpha\beta$ is an element of N and $ab + N = \alpha\beta + N$.

Since R is a module, N is a normal subgroup and the set of residue classes R/N is an additive abelian group whose zero element is the ideal N itself:

$$(a + N) + N = N + (a + N) = a + N$$

(cf. Theorem 8 of Chapter 1).   From Equation 2.17 we see that R/N is closed with respect to multiplication.   Associativity of multiplication follows from

$$
\begin{aligned}
(a + N)[(b + N)(c + N)] &= (a + N)[bc + N] = a(bc) + N \\
&= (ab)c + N = [ab + N](c + N) \\
&= [(a + N)(b + N)](c + N).
\end{aligned}
$$

Distributivity of multiplication with respect to addition on the left follows from

$$
\begin{aligned}
(a + N)[(b + N) + (c + N)] &= (a + N)[(b + c) + N] \\
&= a(b + c) + N \\
&= (ab + ac) + N
\end{aligned}
$$

and

$$
\begin{aligned}
(a + N)(b + N) + (a + N)(c + N) &= ab + N + ac + N \\
&= (ab + ac) + N,
\end{aligned}
$$

with similar equations for the distributivity on the right.   Hence R/N is a ring.

If Z is the ring of integers and N is the ideal of even integers, then the ring Z/N consists of the two elements N and $1 + N$.   That is, the only elements of Z/N are the identity of the group and the unity element of the ring Z/N.   One can readily prove directly in this concrete example that Z/N is a ring.   For example, closure of addition and multiplication follows from

	N	$1 + N$
N	N	$1 + N$
$1 + N$	$1 + N$	N

and

	N	$1 + N$
N	N	N
$1 + N$	N	$1 + N$

respectively.

2.7 A Fundamental Theorem in Ring Theory

In the previous section we saw that if ϕ was a homomorphism mapping R onto $\bar{R}$, then the preimages of the identity in $\bar{R}$ formed an ideal N in R.   Furthermore we showed that if N were *any* ideal in R, then the set of residue classes R/N formed a ring.   We can now prove the analog of the fundamental theorem in group theory (Theorem 10 of Chapter 1) for rings.

Theorem 10.   Let ϕ be a homomorphism mapping R onto $\bar{R}$.   Let N be the set of elements in R which map onto the identity $\bar{0}$ of $\bar{R}$. Then N is an ideal in R and the ring of remainder classes R/N is a ring isomorphic to $\bar{R}$.

Proof: The facts that N is an ideal and R/N is a ring have been established in Theorems 8 and 9, respectively.

We shall show now that the mapping

$$\psi: \qquad a + N \leftrightarrow \bar{a} \tag{2.18}$$

is an isomorphism, where $\phi(a) = \bar{a}$.   Since N is a normal subgroup of the additive group of R, we conclude by Theorem 10 of Chapter 1 that

ψ is one to one. To show that it is an isomorphism we need only write

$$\psi((a + N) + (b + N)) = \psi(a + b + N) = \overline{a + b} = \phi(a + b)$$
$$= \phi(a) + \phi(b) = \bar{a} + \bar{b}$$
$$= \psi(a + N) + \psi(b + N)$$

and

$$\psi((a + N)(b + N)) = \psi(ab + N) = \overline{ab} = \phi(ab) = \phi(a)\phi(b)$$
$$= \bar{a}\bar{b} = \psi(a + N)\psi(b + N).$$

If N is an ideal in a ring R, then we can consider the mapping

$$\nu: \qquad R \to R/N$$

defined by

$$\nu: \qquad a \to a + N$$

for all a in R. We shall show in Theorem 11 that ν is a homomorphism. It is called the *natural homomorphism* of R onto R/N.

Theorem 11. Let N be an ideal in a ring R and let ν,

$$\nu: \qquad a \to a + N,$$

be a mapping of R onto R/N. Then ν is a homomorphism.

Proof: For any a, b in R we have

$$\nu(a + b) = a + b + N = (a + N) + (b + N) = \nu(a) + \nu(b)$$

and

$$\nu(ab) = ab + N = (a + N)(b + N) = \nu(a)\nu(b).$$

Hence,

$$\nu: \qquad R \to R/N$$

is a homomorphism.

2.8 Ideals

The theory of ideals plays an extremely important rôle in ring theory. We shall investigate various special types of ideals and see how they aid in the determination of the structure of abstract rings. Our work on fields in the next chapter will rest heavily on the concepts concerning ideals which we are about to develop.

If R is a ring, N_1 and N_2 ideals in R, then by the *intersection* of N_1 and N_2, written $N_1 \cap N_2$, we mean the set of all elements common to both N_1 and N_2, (cf. Section 1.11). We leave as an exercise for the reader the proof of the fact that $N_1 \cap N_2$ is an ideal.

If M is any set of elements in a ring R, we can find ideals which contain M. For example, the ring R itself is an ideal containing any subset of R.

Definition. Let R be a ring and let M be an arbitrary subset of R. The intersection of all ideals containing this set M is called the ideal generated by M and is written (M).

Clearly (M) is the *smallest* ideal containing all elements of the set M. If M is a *finite* set of elements, say $a_1, a_2, \cdots, a_r$; then we write $(a_1, a_2, \cdots, a_r)$ in place of (M). In particular, if M consists of a single element, say a, of the ring R we write (a) in place of (M). An ideal such as (a) generated by a single element of the ring is called a *principal ideal*.

Suppose R is a ring and (a) a principal ideal in R. We shall investigate just what form the elements of (a) must have. Since (a) is closed with respect to addition, all terms of the form $a + a$, $a + a + a$, $\cdots$ must be in (a). Hence (a) must contain all elements of the form na, where n is a positive integer. Since (a) is a group, 0 must be in (a). Therefore even if n is zero, na is in (a). Also, since (a) is a module $-a$, the inverse of a is in (a) and $(-a) + (-a) + \cdots + (-a)$ which we shall write as na with $n < 0$ is also in (a). (Cf. Theorem 2 for a discussion of na.)

An ideal (a), being a subring is closed with respect to multiplication. Therefore aa, aaa, $\cdots$ are elements in (a). We write these as a^2, a^3, $\cdots$, or in general a^m is in (a), where m is a *positive* integer. Since (a) may not have a unity, a^0 may not be in (a), and since (a) does not necessarily have multiplicative inverses, a^m with $m < 0$ will not necessarily be in (a).

So far we have utilized the properties of a subring. Futhermore, (a) is an ideal. Hence it contains all elements of the form ra and ar', where r and r' are arbitrary elements in the ring R. We see that all elements of the form

$$na + a^m + ra + ar' \tag{2.19}$$

must be in (a), where n is an integer, positive, negative, or zero and m is a positive integer. Actually, the term a^m in Equation 2.19 is redundant. If $m = 1$, then we may write $na + a^m$ as $(n + 1)a$. If $m \geq 2$, then $a^m = a^{m-1}a$ and we may write

$$a^{m-1}a + ra = (a^{m-1} + r)a = r''a$$

where r'' is some ring element.

We see therefore, that any ideal containing a must also contain all elements of the form

$$na + ra + ar' \tag{2.20}$$

and perhaps others.

If in particular R is a commutative ring, then $ar' = r'a$ and we may write Equation 2.20 simply as $na + (r + r')a$, or

$$na + sa \qquad\qquad (2.21)$$

where s is a ring element.   In this case the totality of elements of the form of Equation 2.21 forms an ideal N.

Since a is an element in N and any ideal containing a must certainly contain N, we conclude that $(a) = N$, that is, N is the ideal generated by a.

If we impose the additional condition on R that it be a commutative ring with *unity element*, then even the term na in Equation 2.21 becomes superfluous; for if e is in N,

$$na = (ne)a$$

and ne is a ring element.   Hence Equation 2.21 becomes

$$na + sa = (ne + s)a = ra,$$

where r is a ring element.   We see, therefore, that if R is a commutative ring with a unity element, the principal ideal (a) generated by a consists simply of all ring multiples ra.

For example, consider the number 4 in the ring of integers Z.   The ideal (4) generated by 4 in Z is a principal ideal and is simply all multiples of 4:

$$(4): \qquad \{0, \pm\, 4, \pm\, 8, \pm\, 12, \cdots\}.$$

If a ring R has a unity element e, then the ideal generated by e is the whole ring, that is, $(e) = R$, since every ring element r may be written as re.   For this reason the ring itself is called the *unit ideal*. For example, if Z is the ring of integers, $Z = (1)$.   The ideal generated by the group identity, namely (0), consists of the zero element alone and is called the *null ideal*.

Other special types of ideals which have many interesting properties are *prime ideals* and *maximal ideals*.

Definition.   Let R be a ring and N an ideal in R.   If N has the property that whenever ab is in N then either a or b is in N; then N is called a *prime ideal*.

For example, the principal ideal (7) is prime in the ring of integers Z, since if $\alpha\beta$ is in (7), α or β must be a multiple of 7.   On the other hand, (6) is not a prime ideal in Z since, in particular, $12 = 4 \cdot 3$ is in (6), yet neither 4 nor 3 is an element of (6).   [Note that 7 is a prime number, while 6 is not.   Later (Section 2.13) we shall prove general theorems of which these examples will be special cases.]

In Section 1.11 of Chapter 1 we defined *maximal* subgroups. The corresponding definition for ideals is the expected one.

Definition. An ideal N in a ring R is said to be *maximal* if there exists no ideal properly contained in R in which N is itself properly contained.

For example, in the ring of integers Z, the ideal (6) is not maximal, since it is properly contained in the ideal (3), which in turn is properly contained in $(1) = Z$. On the other hand, (7) *is* a maximal ideal since the only ideal containing (7) is Z. General theorems showing the relation of prime and maximal ideals will be developed in the next section.

A convenient notation to adopt in dealing with ideals is the *congruence notation*. This notation can, of course be applied to relatively arbitrary sets, but it is especially useful in ideal theory. Suppose that S is a set (group, ring, etc.) and let a be an element of S. Then we shall write

$$a \equiv 0 \quad (\mathrm{mod}\ S)$$

or simply

$$a \equiv 0 \quad (S).$$

These equations are to be read "a is congruent to zero modulo S." Such a notation is in harmony with that of elementary number theory when we write

$$n \equiv 0 \quad (\mathrm{mod}\ p)$$

if the integer p divides the integer n. (Cf. Example C of Section 1.4 and Example C of Section 1.9, Chapter 1.) Similarly, if α and β are any two elements in S whose difference $\alpha - \beta$ is in S, we write

$$\alpha \equiv \beta \quad (S)$$

or

$$\alpha - \beta \equiv 0 \quad (S).$$

This again is an extension of the congruence notation of number theory.

If R is a ring and N is an ideal in R, then the elements of the residue class ring R/N are of the form $a + N$, where a is an element of R. In Theorem 11 we proved the existence of a natural homomorphism ν of R onto R/N. Now an equation such as

$$\nu(ab) = \nu(c) \tag{2.22}$$

or

$$(a + N)(b + N) = c + N$$

in R/N becomes a congruence,

$$ab \equiv c \quad (N), \tag{2.23}$$

in R. In short, equalities in R/N become congruences in R.

If N is an ideal and we have

$$a \equiv b \quad (N) \tag{2.24}$$

and

$$c \equiv d \quad (N) \tag{2.25}$$

then $a + c \equiv b + d$ (N) and $ac \equiv bd$ (N).   Hence we see that congruences can be added and multiplied together like equalities.   To prove these statements we note that Equations 2.24 and 2.25 may be written as

$$a = b + n' \qquad c = d + n'', \tag{2.26}$$

where n' and n'' are elements in N.   Adding the above equations, we have $(a + c) = (b + d) + n' + n''$.   Since N is closed with respect to addition, $n' + n''$ is an element in N and hence

$$(a + c) \equiv (b + d) \quad (N).$$

Similarly, if we multiply Equations 2.26 together we obtain $ac = bd + bn'' + n'd + n'n''$.   Since N is an ideal, bn'', $n'd$, and $n'n''$ are all elements of N and hence

$$ac \equiv bd \quad (N).$$

As a corollary to this last result we have

$$ra \equiv rb \quad (N),$$

where r is any ring element.   This follows from the equation

$$r \equiv r \quad (N)$$

which is certainly true since the group identity 0 of R is in N.

Another shorthand notation for expressing the fact that an element a is a member of a set S is the following.   Let S be a set and a an element of S.   We shall express this property by writing

$$a \in S.$$

The equation is read : "a is an element of S."   If b is *not* an element of S we shall write $b \notin S$.

The notation $A \subset B$ (cf. Section 1.11 of Chapter 1) will still be retained to mean A is a *subset* of B.   That is, if A and B are *sets* we use the "inclusion symbols" $\subset$, $\subseteq$, $\supset$, $\supseteq$; while if A is an element and B is a set we use the "element of" symbols $\in$ or $\notin$.

2.9 Prime Ideals

If R is a ring and N is an ideal in R, we have investigated the concept of the ring of residue classes R/N.   It may be that if the ideal has some special properties, for example, the property of being prime or maximal, the ring of remainder classes may also have some additional properties. For example, in Section 2.6 we considered Z/N, where Z was the ring of integers and N was the ideal of even integers, $N = (2)$. The elements of Z/N were $\{N, 1 + N\}$ and formed a field. We also see that N is principal, prime, and maximal. These considerations lead us to the following theorems.

Theorem 12. Let R be a commutative ring with a unity element and let N be an ideal in R. Then the ring of remainder classes R/N is an integral domain if and only if N is a prime ideal.

Proof: If $N = R$, then $R/N = (0)$ and the theorem is trivial. Suppose $N \neq R$. Then R/N has at least two elements. Since the mapping $\nu: R \rightarrow R/N$ is a homomorphism by Theorem 11 and R is commutative with unity, we easily see that R/N also has these properties. Suppose now that N is prime. Then by the very definition of an integral domain, all we need show is that R/N has no divisors of zero. The residue classes of R/N are of the form $a + N$, $b + N$, where a and b are elements of R.

Suppose $(a + N)(b + N) = N$, that is, the product of two elements in the ring of remainder classes is null. We shall show that this implies either $a + N$ or $b + N$ (or both) is the zero element of R/N, that is, either $a + N = N$ or $b + N = N$. By definition of multiplication of residue classes $(a + N)(b + N) = ab + N$. But $(a + N)(b + N) = N$. Hence $ab + N = N$. In our congruence notation we may write $ab \equiv 0 \ (N)$ since ab is an element of N. But by definition of a prime ideal, if ab is in N, either a or b is in N. Hence, either $a \equiv 0 \ (N)$ or $b \equiv 0 \ (N)$. Since either $a \in N$ or $b \in N$, we have either $a + N = N$ or $b + N = N$. Hence $a + N$ or $b + N$ must be the zero element in R/N.

Conversely, suppose R/N is an integral domain and let a and b be any two elements in R such that ab is in N. Since $ab \in N$, we have the equation $(a + N)(b + N) = ab + N = N$ in the ring of residue classes. Since R/N is an integral domain and the product of the two elements $a + N$ and $b + N$ is zero, either $a + N$ or $b + N$ is zero. That is, either $a + N = N$ or $b + N = N$. Hence either a or b is an element in N and by definition of a prime ideal, N is prime.

We have seen that if R is a commutative ring with unity and N is an ideal in R, then the ring of remainder classes R/N is also a commutative ring with a unity element. However, nothing can be said about the divisors of zero property. That is, R/N may have divisors of zero and yet R may be an integral domain and conversely. In the above theorem nothing was said about the divisors of zero of R. Yet whether it had or did not have divisors of zero, R/N was an integral domain if and only if N were prime.

For example, Z is an integral domain. The ideal (6) is not prime in Z. Hence by the above theorem $Z/(6)$ is not an integral domain. In this example we can verify the theorem directly. The elements of $Z/(6)$ are

$$(6)$$
$$1 + (6)$$
$$2 + (6)$$
$$3 + (6)$$
$$4 + (6)$$
$$5 + (6).$$

Clearly neither $2 + (6)$ nor $3 + (6)$ is the zero element (6) of $Z/(6)$, yet

$$[2 + (6)][3 + (6)] = 6 + (6) = (6)$$

is the zero element and hence $Z/(6)$ has divisors of zero.

Again let R be the totality of all pairs of real numbers where addition and multiplication of pairs (a,b) and (α,β) are defined by the equations

$$(a,b) + (\alpha,\beta) = (a + \alpha, b + \beta),$$
$$(a,b)(\alpha,\beta) = (a\alpha, b\beta).$$

We saw in Section 2.3 that R had divisors of zero. Clearly R is commutative with unity $(1,1)$. Now the totality of elements of the form $(a,0)$ is an ideal N in R, and N is a prime ideal, for if

$$(a,b)(\alpha,\beta) \in N$$

then $(a,b)(\alpha,\beta) = (a\alpha,b\beta) = (a\alpha,0)$. Since $b\beta = 0$ and b and β are real numbers, either b or β is zero and hence either (a,b) or (α,β) is an element of N. By Theorem 12, R/N is an integral domain and hence free of divisors of zero.

If we require N to be a *maximal* ideal we can prove the stronger result.

Theorem 13. Let R be a commutative ring with a unity element and let N be an ideal in R. Then the ring of remainder classes R/N is a field if and only if N is a maximal ideal.

Proof: Suppose N is a maximal ideal in R. Then $N \subset R$ by the very definition of maximal. Hence R/N has at least two elements. For simplicity in notation let $\bar{R} = R/N$ be the ring of residue classes. If x is an element in R, then under the homomorphism $\nu : R \to \bar{R}$, $\nu(x) = x + N$. Call this element $\bar{x}$, that is, $\bar{x} = x + N$. In particular $\bar{0} = 0 + N = N$.

Let e be the unity element in R. We must show that if $\bar{r}$ is any nonzero element in $\bar{R}$, that is, $\bar{r} \in \bar{R}$ and $\bar{r} \neq \bar{0}$, then there exists an element $\bar{s}$ in $\bar{R}$ such that $\bar{r}\bar{s} = \bar{e}$. Since $\bar{r} \neq \bar{0}$, $r \notin N$, since if $r \in N$ then $\bar{r} = r + N = N = \bar{0}$. Consider the ideal (r,N) generated by r and N. Since N is maximal and $r \notin N$, (r,N) must be the whole ring R, $R = (r,N)$. Therefore every element in R can be expressed in the form $sr + n$, where $s \in R$ and $n \in N$. (Recall that R is a commutative ring with a unity element.) In particular the unity e in R has this property,

$$e = sr + n.$$

Hence $e \equiv sr \quad (N)$, since $e - sr$ is an element in N. But this is equivalent to $(e + N) = (s + N)(r + N)$ in R/N, or to $\bar{e} = \bar{s}\bar{r}$ in $\bar{R}$, as was desired to be proved.

Conversely, suppose R/N is a field. We shall assume that N is not maximal and arrive at a contradiction. Since N is not maximal, there exists an ideal M in R such that

$$N \subset M \subset R.$$

Let a be an arbitrary element in R and let b be an element in M which is not in N. Under the homomorphism $\nu : R \to R/N$, $\nu(a) = a + N$. If we let $R/N \equiv \bar{R}$ as above then we may let $\bar{a} = a + N$. Since $\bar{R}$ is a field, there exists an element $\bar{c}$ in $\bar{R}$ such that $\bar{b}\bar{c} = \bar{a}$, or in congruence notation $bc \equiv a \quad (N)$. [$\bar{b} \neq \bar{0}$ since $b \notin N$. Hence we may set $\bar{c} = \bar{b}^{-1}\bar{a}$, $\bar{b}^{-1}$ existing since $\bar{R}$ is a field.] Now $N \subset M$; hence the equation $bc \equiv a \quad (M)$ is certainly true. But $b \in M$. Therefore $bc \equiv 0 \quad (M)$, or $a \equiv 0 \quad (M)$. That is, a is an element in M. But a was an arbitrary element in R. Therefore $M = R$ and N is maximal.

As a corollary to the above theorems, we see that every maximal ideal is prime, that is:

Corollary. If R is a commutative ring with a unity element and N is a maximal ideal in R, then N is a prime ideal.

The converse of this corollary is not true. That is, there exist prime ideals which are not maximal. We shall show, for example, in the next section that the principal ideal (x) in the ring of polynomials $Z[x]$ is prime but not maximal.

2.10 Polynomial Rings

The topic we are about to consider, namely polynomial rings, is one of the most important, and in the opinion of the writer, one of the most fascinating topics in ring theory. Many of the results of elementary algebra, for example, the unique factorization theorem of polynomials in one variable with real numbers as coefficients, are but special cases of general theorems which we shall prove.

We consider a commutative ring R and ordered sets of elements in R, for example,

$$(a_0, a_1, a_2, \cdots), \tag{2.27}$$

where $a_0, a_1, a_2, \cdots$ are elements in R. We shall consider only arrays of the form of Equation 2.27, where all but a finite number of the a_k are equal to zero. If we let x be a symbol, not an element of R, we may write Equation 2.27 as

$$a_0 x^0 + a_1 x + a_2 x^2 + \cdots \tag{2.28}$$

This is not to be construed as multiplying a_k by x^k and adding it to $a_{k+1} x^{k+1}$. The x^k are simply to be considered as a notation for indicating the order of the a_k elements in the array of Equation 2.27. We have done such manipulations before. For example, a complex number a can be written as an ordered pair of real numbers α and β:

$$a = (\alpha, \beta)$$

or again as

$$a = \alpha + i\beta$$

where $i = \sqrt{-1}$.

A compact way of writing Equation 2.28 is

$$\sum_k a_k x^k \tag{2.29}$$

and this expression, in analogy with elementary algebra, is called a *polynomial* in x, and the a_k are called the *coefficients* of the polynomial. The symbol x is called an *indeterminate*. We denote the set of all polynomials in x over R by $R[x]$. In brief, then, we have the following definition.

Definition. Let R be a commutative ring and x an indeterminate. The set of all polynomials $f(x)$,

$$f(x) = \sum_k a_k x^k = a_0 x^0 + a_1 x + a_2 x^2 + \cdots$$

where the a_k are elements of the ring R and only a finite number of them are unequal to zero, is called $R[x]$.

In Theorem 14 below, after we have defined addition and multiplication of polynomials, we shall prove that $R[x]$ is a *ring*.

It will be assumed that the indeterminate x commutes with all ring elements a, that is, ax and xa represent the same quantity. The terms "polynomial" and "coefficient" are those used in elementary algebra. The further definitions we are about to make are in harmony with our earlier intuitive notions of manipulating polynomials.

   Definition.   Let R be a commutative ring and x an indeterminate. Let

$$f(x) = \sum_k a_k x^k, \qquad a_k \in R,$$

and

$$g(x) = \sum_k b_k x^k, \qquad b_k \in R$$

be any two polynomials in $R[x]$.

   (i) The polynomials $f(x)$ and $g(x)$ are said to be *equal*, written $f(x) = g(x)$ if and only if $a_j = b_j$ for every j.
   (ii) By the *sum* of $f(x)$ and $g(x)$, written $f(x) + g(x)$, we mean

$$\psi(x) = \sum_k (a_k + b_k) x^k.$$

Clearly $f(x) + g(x) = \psi(x)$ is also a polynomial, since $(a_k + b_k) \in R$.
   (iii) The *zero polynomial* $\phi(x)$,

$$\phi(x) = \sum_k c_k x^k$$

is the polynomial in which $c_k = 0$ for every k, $k = 0, 1, 2, \cdots$.
   (iv) The *product* of two polynomials $f(x)$ and $g(x)$, written $f(x)g(x)$ is defined as

$$h(x) = (\sum_j a_j x^j)(\sum_k b_k x^k) = \sum_m c_m x^m,$$

where

$$c_m = \sum_{j+k=m} a_j b_k.$$

Note that only a finite number of the c_m are different from zero. Clearly $f(x)g(x) = h(x)$ is also a polynomial, since c_m, being the sum of products of elements in R, is also in R.
   (v) The *degree of the polynomial* $f(x)$ is the largest integer α for which a_α is unequal to zero. We do not assign a degree to the zero polynomial.
   On the basis of these definitions we can prove that the set $R[x]$ is a ring (cf. Theorem 14). This ring is called "the ring of polynomials over R in the indeterminate x" or simply the "ring of polynomials over R." The process of adjoining the indeterminate x to the ring R in order to form the ring of polynomials $R[x]$ is called *ring adjunction*. Later (cf. the next chapter) we shall introduce the concept of "field

adjunction." We shall always use square brackets [ ] for ring adjunctions and reserve parentheses ( ) for field adjunctions.

Theorem 14. Let R be a commutative ring and let x be an indeterminate. Then the set $R[x]$ is a commutative ring.

Proof: We shall first show that $R[x]$ is a module. Closure of addition follows from (ii) of the above definition. Associativity follows from the corresponding property in R, viz.: if

$$f(x) = \textstyle\sum a_k x^k$$
$$g(x) = \textstyle\sum b_k x^k$$
$$h(x) = \textstyle\sum c_k x^k$$

then

$$f + (g + h) = \textstyle\sum [a_k + (b_k + c_k)]x^k = \textstyle\sum [(a_k + b_k) + c_k]x^k$$
$$= (f + g) + h.$$

The identity element is the zero polynomial $\phi(x) = \sum 0 x^k$, since

$$f(x) + \phi(x) = \textstyle\sum (a_k + 0)x^k = \textstyle\sum a_k x^k = f(x).$$

The inverse of $f(x)$ is

$$\textstyle\sum (- a_k)x^k \tag{2.30}$$

since

$$\textstyle\sum a_k x^k + \textstyle\sum (- a_k)x^k = \textstyle\sum [a_k + (- a_k)]x^k = \textstyle\sum (a_k - a_k)x^k = \textstyle\sum 0 x^k = \phi(x).$$

Hence $R[x]$ is an additive group. We shall hereafter write 0 for the zero polynomial

$$0 = \textstyle\sum 0 x^k.$$

It will be clear from the context whether the 0 is the zero element of the ring R or the zero polynomial. Also we shall write Equation 2.30 as $- \sum a_k x^k$ and call it $- f(x)$.

The fact that $R[x]$ is abelian follows from the corresponding property in R, viz.:

$$f(x) + g(x) = \textstyle\sum (a_k + b_k)x^k = \textstyle\sum (b_k + a_k)x^k = g(x) + f(x).$$

We now see that $R[x]$ is a module. Closure of multiplication follows from (iv) of the above definition. Associativity of multiplication, distributivity of multiplication with respect to addition, and commutativity of multiplication follow from the corresponding properties in R and are merely exercises in high school algebra. For example, commutativity follows from

$$f(x)g(x) = (\textstyle\sum_k a_k x^k)(\textstyle\sum_j b_j x^j) = \textstyle\sum_m (\textstyle\sum_{k+j=m} a_k b_j)x^m = \textstyle\sum_m (\textstyle\sum_{k+j=m} b_j a_k)x^m$$
$$= g(x)f(x).$$

We see therefore that $R[x]$ is a commutative ring. An example of such a ring is $Z[x]$, which is simply all polynomials in the single variable x with integral coefficients, for example,

$$0x^0 - 1 \cdot x + 3x^2 + 0x^3 + 0x^4 - 15x^5 + 0x^6 + 0x^7 + \cdots$$
$$= -x + 3x^2 - 15x^5$$

is such a polynomial.

As a trivial exercise for the reader we leave the proof of the statement that if $R[x]$ is the ring of polynomials over a commutative ring R and S is the set of all polynomials in $R[x]$ of the form $a_0x^0 + 0x + 0x^2 + \cdots$, then S is a ring isomorphic to R. Under this isomorphism we shall identify R with S and write

$$a_0 + a_1x + a_2x^2 + \cdots$$

rather than

$$a_0x^0 + a_1x + a_2x^2 + \cdots$$

Similarly we may write

$$af(x) = a\sum a_kx^k = \sum aa_kx^k$$

rather than

$$ax^0f(x) = ax^0\sum a_kx^k = \sum aa_kx^{k+0} = \sum aa_kx^k,$$

where a is an element of R.

Note that in general x is *not* an element of $R[x]$, since x is not of the form $a\dot{x}$, where a is in R. If, however, R has a *unity element* e, then *ex is an element* of $R[x]$. Since

$$exf(x) = ex\sum a_kx^k = \sum(ea_k)x^{k+1} = \sum a_kx^{k+1}$$

we shall hereafter write simply x instead of ex, realizing of course that by writing x we are assuming that R has a unity.

If R has a unity element e, then $R[x]$ also has a unity, namely ex^0, since

$$ex^0f(x) = ex^0\sum a_kx^k = \sum(ea_k)x^{k+0} = \sum a_kx^k = f(x).$$

Hereafter we shall simply write e for the unity in $R[x]$ (if $e \in R$), the context making it clear as to whether we mean the unity of R or the unity of $R[x]$.

In our definition of a polynomial ring $R[x]$ we assumed x was not an element in R. However, if α is any element in R and $f(x) = \sum a_kx^k$ is an element in $R[x]$, we may consider the set of all elements $f(\alpha) = \sum a_k\alpha^k$. In the above expression $a_k\alpha^k$ is to be interpreted as ring multiplication, that is, as $a_k \cdot \alpha \cdot \alpha \cdots \alpha$ with k of the α factors. Clearly, since R is closed with respect to addition and multiplication, $f(\alpha)$ is an element in R. Let, then, S be that subset of R consisting of all elements in R of the form $f(\alpha)$, where $f(x) \in R[x]$ and α is a fixed element in R. We can prove many interesting theorems concerning such sets. For example, we can show that the mapping $\phi : f(x) \to f(\alpha)$ is a homomorphism. (Cf. Exercise 2.58 at the end of this chapter.)

Many of the properties of a ring R pass over to the polynomial ring $R[x]$. For example, we have seen that if R is commutative, $R[x]$ is commutative; and if R has a unity element, then $R[x]$ also has a unity. The divisors of zero property also goes over to polynomial rings.

Theorem 15. If R is a commutative ring without divisors of zero, then $R[x]$ is also free of divisors of zero.

Proof: We shall assume that $R[x]$ has divisors of zero and obtain a contradiction. If $R[x]$ has divisors of zero, then there exist elements $f(x) = \sum a_j x^j$ and $g(x) = \sum b_k x^k$ in $R[x]$ with $f(x) \neq 0$, $g(x) \neq 0$ such that $f(x)g(x) = 0$. Let the degree of $f(x)$ be α and that of $g(x)$ be β. By definition of the degree of a polynomial, $a_\alpha \neq 0$, $b_\beta \neq 0$. (Since neither $f(x)$ nor $g(x)$ is zero, they both *have* a degree.) Now $f(x)g(x) = \sum c_m x^m$ where $c_m = \sum\limits_{j+k=m} a_j b_k$ by definition of multiplication of polynomials. Since $fg = 0$ we have by the very definition of the zero polynomial that

$$c_m = 0, \qquad m = 0, 1, \cdots, \alpha + \beta.$$

In particular, the coefficient of $x^{\alpha+\beta}$ in $f(x)g(x)$ is $c_{\alpha+\beta} = a_\alpha b_\beta$ and by the above remark, $a_\alpha b_\beta = 0$. But by hypothesis R has no divisors of zero. Hence either $a_\alpha = 0$ or $b_\beta = 0$. This contradicts the statement that $a_\alpha \neq 0$, $b_\beta \neq 0$. Hence $R[x]$ is free of divisors of zero.

If R is a commutative ring and x is an indeterminate which commutes with all ring elements, we have seen that $R[x]$ is also a commutative ring. Consider now another indeterminate y which commutes with all elements (polynomials) in $R[x]$. Then we may consider the ring of polynomials in y which have polynomials in x as coefficients, namely $R[x][y]$. (Since $R[x]$ is a commutative ring, $R[x][y]$ is also a commutative ring by Theorem 14.) One could also consider $R[y]$ and $R[y][x]$. Here $R[y]$ is the ring of polynomials in y, while $R[y][x]$ is the ring of polynomials in x with polynomials in y as coefficients. We easily see that $R[x][y]$ and $R[y][x]$ are the same ring. Hence we simply write $R[x,y]$ and call it the ring of polynomials in the two indeterminates over R.

Similarly we can consider the polynomial ring $R[x_1, x_2, \cdots, x_n]$ in the n indeterminates $x_1, x_2, \cdots, x_n$ over the ring R. We leave as exercises for the reader the proofs of the facts that if R is a commutative ring, so is $R[x_1, x_2, \cdots, x_n]$ and if R has a unity or is free of divisors of zero, then $R[x_1, x_2, \cdots, x_n]$ also has the corresponding property.

To conclude this section we shall actually construct an ideal in $Z[x]$ which is prime but not maximal (cf. the concluding remarks of the previous section).

Let $Z[x]$ be the ring of polynomials over the integers Z. Let (x) be the principal ideal generated by x. We shall show that (x) is prime but not maximal. Suppose $\phi(x)$ and $\psi(x)$ are two elements in $Z[x]$ which have the property that their product $\phi(x)\psi(x)$ is in (x), that is, $\phi(x)\psi(x) \in (x)$. If

$$\phi(x) = a_0 + a_1 x + a_2 x^2 + \cdots, \qquad a_k \in Z$$

and

$$\psi(x) = b_0 + b_1 x + b_2 x^2 + \cdots, \qquad b_k \in Z$$

then by definition of multiplication of polynomials,

$$\phi(x)\psi(x) = a_0 b_0 + (b_0 a_1 + a_0 b_1)x + \cdots. \qquad (2.31)$$

Since $\phi(x)\psi(x)$ is in (x), it must be of the form $xf(x)$, where $f(x)$ is a polynomial in $Z[x]$. (Since $Z[x]$ is a commutative ring with a unity element, the elements in a principal ideal, for example (x), consist solely of ring multiples of x.) Suppose

$$f(x) = c_0 + c_1 x + c_2 x^2 + \cdots, \qquad c_k \in Z.$$

Then

$$xf(x) = c_0 x + c_1 x^2 + c_2 x^3 + \cdots.$$

If this expression is to be the same as Equation 2.31 we must have, in particular, $a_0 b_0 = 0$ by definition of equality of two polynomials. But Z has no divisors of zero. Hence a_0 or b_0 must be equal to zero and either

$$\phi(x) = a_1 x + a_2 x^2 + \cdots = x(a_1 + a_2 x + \cdots)$$

or

$$\psi(x) = b_1 x + b_2 x^2 + \cdots = x(b_1 + b_2 x + \cdots)$$

which implies either $\phi(x)$ or $\psi(x)$ is in (x).

The fact that (x) is prime has now been established. To show that it is *not* maximal, we must exhibit an ideal N such that (x) is properly contained in N, while N itself is properly contained in $Z[x]$. Such an ideal is $(2,x)$. Clearly $(x) \subseteq (2,x) \subseteq Z[x]$. We shall show that the inclusion is _proper_, that is, $(x) \subset (2,x) \subset Z[x]$. To prove the above statement, all we need do is to find an element α in $(2,x)$ but not in (x) and an element β in $Z[x]$ but not in $(2,x)$. The number 2 will serve for α and the number 1 for β.

Clearly $2 \in (2,x)$. We shall show that $2 \notin (x)$. For suppose $2 \in (x)$.

Then 2 may be written in the form $2 = xf(x)$, where $f(x)$ is an element of $Z[x]$, say

$$f(x) = \sum c_k x^k, \qquad c_k \in Z.$$

and we have

$$2 = 0 + c_0 x + c_1 x^2 + c_2 x^3 + \cdots .$$

But this is an impossible equation, since by definition of equality of polynomials we would have to have $2 = 0$, which is false in the ring of integers Z.

To show that $(2,x)$ is properly contained in $Z[x]$, we shall show that 1 is not in $(2,x)$. (Obviously 1 is an element of $Z[x]$.) Suppose $1 \in (2,x)$. Then 1 would have a representation

$$1 = 2f(x) + xg(x)$$

where $f(x)$ and $g(x)$ are ring elements in $Z[x]$, say

$$f(x) = \sum c_k x^k, \qquad c_k \in Z$$
$$g(x) = \sum d_k x^k, \qquad d_k \in Z.$$

We would then have

$$\begin{aligned}
1 &= 2(c_0 + c_1 x + c_2 x^2 + \cdots) + x(d_0 + d_1 x + d_2 x^2 + \cdots) \\
&= 2c_0 + (2c_1 + d_0)x + (2c_2 + d_1)x^2 + \cdots
\end{aligned}$$

and there exists no integer c_0 in Z such that $1 = 2c_0$. Hence (x) is not a maximal ideal in $Z[x]$.

2.11 Principal Ideals

In Section 2.8 we defined a principal ideal as an ideal generated by a single element of a ring. If a commutative ring R has the property that every ideal in it is a principal ideal, we shall call R a *principal ideal ring*, abbreviated, p.i.r.

The ideal $(6,10)$ in the ring of integers Z is a principal ideal; in fact it is the ideal generated by 2,

$$(2) = (6,10).$$

To prove this statement, we note that $6 \in (2)$ and $10 \in (2)$, since $6 = 3 \cdot 2$ and $10 = 5 \cdot 2$, and both 3 and 5 are ring elements in Z. Hence certainly

$$(6,10) \subseteq (2). \tag{2.32}$$

On the other hand, $2 = 2 \cdot 6 - 10$, that is, 2 is of the form $\alpha 6 + \beta 10$, where α and β are elements in Z (namely $\alpha = 2, \beta = -1$). Hence

$$(2) \subseteq (6,10). \tag{2.33}$$

Equations 2.32 and 2.33 show that $(2) = (6,10)$ and therefore $(6,10)$ is actually a principal ideal. We leave as an exercise for the reader the proof of the fact that Z is a p.i.r., that is, every ideal in Z may be written as a principal ideal.

If Δ is a field, then it is certainly a commutative ring and hence $\Delta[x]$, the ring of polynomials over Δ, is defined and is a commutative ring. (Also $\Delta[x]$ has a unity and is free of divisors of zero.) Suppose N is an ideal in $\Delta[x]$. Then N consists of polynomials, for example $f(x) = \sum a_k x^k$. Now among all elements $f(x)$ of N there exist polynomials of degree α such that every polynomial $f(x)$ in N is of degree greater than or equal to α. Any polynomial of degree α will be said to be a polynomial of *minimal degree*, that is, there exist polynomials of degree greater than or equal to α, but there exist no polynomials of degree less than α in N. (Recall that we do not assign a degree to the polynomial identically zero.) With this definition we may now prove:

Theorem 16. If Δ is a field and x an indeterminate, then the ring of polynomials $\Delta[x]$ over Δ is a principal ideal ring.

Proof: Let N be an arbitrary ideal in $\Delta[x.]$ We wish to show that N is a principal ideal. If N is the null ideal $N = (0)$, the theorem is trivial since the ideal only has a single element. Suppose N is not null. Then there exist nonzero polynomials $f(x)$ in N. Let $g(x)$ be any polynomial in N of minimal degree m. We shall show that $N = (g(x))$, that is, that $g(x)$ generates N. Since $\Delta[x]$ is commutative with a unity element we need show only that every element $f(x)$ in N may be expressed in the form $f(x) = r(x)g(x)$, where $r(x)$ is a ring element in $\Delta[x]$. Let, then, $f(x)$ be an arbitrary element in N of degree n.

Explicitly,

$$g(x) = a_0 x^m + a_1 x^{m-1} + \cdots + a_m, \qquad a_k \in \Delta$$
$$f(x) = b_0 x^n + b_1 x^{n-1} + \cdots + b_n, \qquad b_k \in \Delta.$$

Since $g(x)$ is of degree m, $a_0 \neq 0$, and since $f(x)$ is of degree n, $b_0 \neq 0$. Further since $g(x)$ is of minimal degree, $n \geq m$.

Consider now the polynomial $p(x)$:

$$p(x) = f(x) - (b_0 a_0^{-1} x^{n-m})g(x). \tag{2.34}$$

Here $p(x)$ is an element of N, since N is an ideal and $f(x)$ and $g(x)$ are in N. [Note that a_0^{-1} exists, since $a_0 \neq 0$ and Δ is a field.] Clearly from Equation 2.34 we see that $p(x)$ is either identically zero or a polynomial of degree less than n.

If $n = m$, then $p(x)$ is of degree less than m or zero. Since m is minimal, $p(x)$ cannot be of degree less than m. Hence in this case $p(x)$ is identically zero and $f(x)$ is a multiple of $g(x)$, namely,

$$f(x) = b_0 a_0^{-1} g(x).$$

Consider now the case in which $n > m$. Then $p(x)$ may be zero or a polynomial of degree (say p) less than n and greater than or equal to m. If $p(x) = 0$, our theorem is proved. If $p(x) \neq 0$ we may treat it in the same fashion as we did $f(x)$ and write

$$q(x) = p(x) - (p_0 a_0^{-1} x^{p-m}) g(x)$$

where p_0 is the leading coefficient of $p(x)$. As before, $q(x)$ is of degree q less than p or else $q(x)$ is identically zero. Since $n > p > q$, we may continue the process a finite number of times to arrive at

$$n > p > q > \cdots > r$$

where r is the degree of a polynomial $r(x)$ with leading coefficient r_0, which has the property that

$$r(x) = (r_0 a_0^{-1} x^{r-m}) g(x).$$

Hence

$$f(x) = (b_0 a_0^{-1} x^{n-m} + p_0 a_0^{-1} x^{p-m} + \cdots + r_0 a_0^{-1} x^{r-m}) g(x),$$

or $f(x) = \psi(x) g(x)$, where $\psi(x) = b_0 a_0^{-1} x^{n-m} + p_0 a_0^{-1} x^{p-m} + \cdots + r_0 a_0^{-1} x^{r-m}$ is an element of $\Delta[x]$. We conclude that N is a principal ideal. Since N was an arbitrary ideal in $\Delta[x]$, the ring $\Delta[x]$ is a p.i.r.

An example of such a ring is the set of all polynomials in the single variable x with real numbers as coefficients.

Not every ring is a p.i.r. For example, the ring of polynomials over Z is not a p.i.r. To prove this statement we shall show, in particular, that $(2,x)$ is not principal. Suppose $(2,x)$ were a principal ideal in the ring $Z[x]$. Then there would exist an element $g(x)$ in $Z[x]$ such that $(g(x)) = (2,x)$. In particular $2 \in (g(x))$, $x \in (g(x))$, and hence there exist elements $\phi(x)$ and $\psi(x)$ in $Z[x]$ such that

$$2 = \phi(x) g(x), \qquad x = \psi(x) g(x). \tag{2.35}$$

From Equations 2.35 we conclude that $x\phi(x) = 2\psi(x)$. Hence the coefficients of $\phi(x)$ must all be even. Thus $\phi(x) = 2\omega(x)$ where $\omega(x)$ is some polynomial in $Z[x]$. From this fact and the first of Equations 2.35 we conclude that $2 = 2\omega(x) g(x)$, and since $Z[x]$ has no divisors of zero, $\omega(x) g(x) = 1$. Hence $1 \in (g(x))$. But $(1) = Z[x]$. Therefore $Z[x] \subseteq (g(x))$, and since $Z[x]$ is the whole ring, $Z[x] = (g(x))$. However, we saw in the last section that $1 \notin (2,x)$; hence we have a contradiction and $(2,x)$ is not a principal ideal in $Z[x]$.

2.12 Euclidean Rings

Many general definitions and theorems which exist in ring theory stem from an attempt to generalize various phenomena in simple concrete rings such as Z and the rings of polynomials over the real and complex fields. A fundamental property of the integers and polynomials is the division algorithm. That is, for example, if a and b are integers, then there exist integers q and r such that

$$a = qb + r \tag{2.36}$$

where $0 \leq r < b$. An attempt to generalize this idea to arbitrary rings leads us to the definition of a *Euclidean ring*.

We shall prove many interesting theorems concerning such rings. In particular we shall consider in abstract rings the analog of the "Euclidean algorithm," the definition of prime elements and factorization theorems.

Definition. Let R be a commutative ring. If we can assign to every nonzero ring element a a nonnegative integer $g(a)$ such that:

(i) For $ab \neq 0$, $g(ab) \geq g(a)$.

(ii) To every two ring elements $a \neq 0$ and b there exist two elements q and r in R such that $b = qa + r$ and in this expression either $g(r) < g(a)$ or $r = 0$,
then: we say R is a *Euclidean ring*.

The second part of the above definition is known as the "division algorithm" and represents the generalization of Equation 2.36 for integers. If we let $g(a) = |a|$, where a is an integer not zero, then we can readily show that Z is a Euclidean ring. In fact we can prove the more general theorem that every Euclidean ring is a p.i.r. (cf. Theorem 17). The converse is not true, that is, not every p.i.r. is a Euclidean ring. The ring of even integers is a p.i.r. which is not Euclidean.

Theorem 17. Every Euclidean ring is a principal ideal ring.

Proof: Let E be a Euclidean ring and N an ideal in E. If N is the null ideal, it is certainly a principal ideal. Suppose N is distinct from the null ideal. Then there exist elements in N unequal to zero. Choose a nonzero element a in N such that $g(a)$ is minimal, that is, there exists no element c in N such that $g(c) < g(a)$. We shall show that the principal ideal generated by a is precisely N.

For every element b in N, there exist elements q and r in E such that $b = qa + r$. Since b, a and qa are in N, so is $b - qa$. Therefore $r \in N$; and since E is a Euclidean ring, either $g(r) < g(a)$ or $r = 0$. Since $g(a)$ is minimal, we must have $r = 0$. Hence $b = qa$. Every element b in N is therefore a multiple of the generating element a

and $N \subseteq (a)$.   Clearly $(a) \subseteq N$ since $a \in N$, and hence N is a principal ideal.

In the above proof we saw that *any* element in N was a multiple of the generator a.   In particular, a itself has this property.   This remark leads us to the following theorem.

Theorem 18.   Every Euclidean ring possesses a unity element.

Proof: Let E be a Euclidean ring.   By the previous theorem we know that E is also a p.i.r.   Hence, in particular, E, the unit ideal, is itself a principal ideal.   Let a be the generator of E, $(a) = E$.   From the previous proof we see that every element in E is a ring multiple of a. In particular, a has this property.   Therefore there exists an element α in E such that

$$a = \alpha a = a\alpha.$$

Now if b is *any* element in E, there exists an element q in E such that $b = qa$.   Hence $b = qa = q(a\alpha) = (qa)\alpha = b\alpha$, and α must be the unity element.

In the previous section we saw that the ring of polynomials over a field $\varDelta$ was a p.i.r.   It is also true that every field is a p.i.r. (cf. the exercises at the end of this chapter).   We can, however, now prove the stronger theorems that $\varDelta$ and $\varDelta[x]$ are Euclidean rings.

Theorem 19.   A field is a Euclidean ring.

Proof: Let $\varDelta$ be a field.   To every element distinct from the zero element, assign the integer zero.   That is, if $a \neq 0$, let $g(a) = 0$.   We shall show that with this g function $\varDelta$ becomes a Euclidean ring.

If a and b are two nonzero elements in $\varDelta$, then $g(ab) = g(a) = g(b) = 0$ and (i) of the definition of a Euclidean ring is satisfied. Further, if $a \neq 0$ and b are any elements in $\varDelta$, then $b = qa + 0$; since $\varDelta$ is a field and $a \neq 0$, and we may let $q = ba^{-1}$.   Hence we see (ii) of the definition of a Euclidean ring is also verified.

Our next theorem is that $\varDelta[x]$ is also a Euclidean ring.

Theorem 20.   If $\varDelta$ is a field and x is an indeterminate, then the ring of polynomials $\varDelta[x]$ over $\varDelta$ is a Euclidean ring.

Proof: If $\phi(x)$ is a nonzero polynomial in $\varDelta[x]$, let $g(\phi) = m$, where m is the degree of $\phi(x)$.   With this g function we shall show that $\varDelta[x]$ is a Euclidean ring.

Suppose $\phi(x)$ and $\psi(x)$ are two polynomials in $\varDelta[x]$ of degrees m and n, respectively.   Then $g(\phi) = m$, $g(\psi) = n$ and $g(\phi\psi) = m + n$ by definition of multiplication of polynomials.   Hence $g(\phi\psi) \geq g(\phi)$.

In order to establish the division algorithm, let

$$\phi(x) = a_0 x^m + a_1 x^{m-1} + \cdots + a_m \in \Delta[x], \qquad a_0 \neq 0$$
$$\psi(x) = b_0 x^n + b_1 x^{n-1} + \cdots + b_n \in \Delta[x], \qquad b_0 \neq 0$$

and assume, without loss of generality,[*] that $n \geq m$. Consider now the polynomial $p(x)$,

$$p(x) = \psi(x) - (b_0 a_0^{-1} x^{n-m})\phi(x).$$

Since $n \geq m$, $p(x)$ is a polynomial of degree p with p less than n, or else $p(x)$ is identically zero. We may write the above equation as $\psi(x) = (b_0 a_0^{-1} x^{n-m})\phi(x) + p(x)$. If $p(x)$ is identically zero, or $p < m$, we have our result. If not, let $p(x) = c_0 x^p + c_1 x^{p-1} + \cdots + c_p$ be an element in $\Delta[x]$, $c_0 \neq 0$ where $p \leq n - 1$. Then if we let $q(x) = p(x) - (c_0 a_0^{-1} x^{p-m})\phi(x)$, we have $p(x) = q(x) + (c_0 a_0^{-1} x^{p-m})\phi(x)$. Now $q(x)$ is of degree $q < p$ or identically zero. If $q(x)$ is identically zero, then $\psi(x) = (b_0 a_0^{-1} x^{n-m} + c_0 a_0^{-1} x^{p-m})\phi(x) + 0$ and our theorem is proved. If $q(x)$ is not zero, it is of degree at most $n - 2$ and $\psi(x) = (b_0 a_0^{-1} x^{n-m} + c_0 a_0^{-1} x^{p-m})\phi(x) + q(x)$. If q is less than m, our theorem is proved. If not, we can continue this process a finite number of times to arrive at $\psi(x) = F(x)\phi(x) + s(x)$, where $F(x) = b_0 a_0^{-1} x^{n-m} + c_0 a_0^{-1} x^{p-m} + \cdots + e_0 a_0^{-1} x^{r-m}$ is an element of $\Delta[x]$, and $s(x)$ is either identically zero or of degree less than m. That is, either $s(x) \equiv 0$ or $g(s) < g(\phi)$, and the division algorithm is established.

Note that the above proof follows along lines similar to those used in establishing the fact that $\Delta[x]$ was a p.i.r. Since by Theorem 17 every Euclidean ring is a p.i.r., Theorem 16 of Section 2.11 can now be considered a corollary to the above theorem.

We now turn to a consideration of another interesting Euclidean ring. Let G be the set of all complex numbers $a + ib$, where a and b are integers (elements of Z) and $i = \sqrt{-1}$. We call $a + ib$ a *Gaussian integer*. Under the usual definitions of addition and multiplication of complex numbers, G can be shown to be an integral domain (cf. the exercises at the end of this chapter). We shall now show that G is a Euclidean ring.

Theorem 21. The ring of Gaussian integers is a Euclidean ring.

Proof: If $\alpha = a + ib$ and $\beta = c + id$ are two Gaussian integers, then $\alpha + \beta = (a + c) + i(b + d)$ and $\alpha\beta = (ac - bd) + i(bc + ad)$ by definition of addition and multiplication of complex numbers. We shall now show that relative to the g function,

$$g(\alpha) = a^2 + b^2, \tag{2.37}$$

---

[*] If $n < m$, then $\psi(x) = 0 \cdot \phi(x) + \psi(x)$ and $g(\psi) < g(\phi)$. Thus (ii) of the definition of a Euclidean ring is satisfied.

the ring of Gaussian integers G forms a Euclidean ring. In our proof we shall have occasion to deal with "Gaussian rational numbers," that is, complex numbers $h = h' + ih''$, where h' and h'' are rational numbers. Since it will be convenient to apply the g function to these numbers as well, we shall define $g(h)$ as

$$g(h) = h'^2 + h''^2.$$

If in particular, h' and h'' are integers, the above definition reduces to that of Equation 2.37.

Since $g(\alpha)$ is the sum of squares of integers, it is itself clearly a nonnegative integer. If α and β are any two nonzero elements of G, then

$$g(\alpha\beta) = (ac - bd)^2 + (bc + ad)^2 = (a^2 + b^2)(c^2 + d^2) = g(\alpha)g(\beta)$$

and $g(\alpha\beta) \geqq g(\alpha)$.

In order to show the existence of a division algorithm, we must find a Gaussian integer ζ such that for each $\alpha \neq 0$ and β in G, $\beta = \zeta\alpha + \omega$ with $g(\omega) < g(\alpha)$ or $\omega = 0$. To find such a ζ we proceed as follows. Define a complex number ζ' by the equation

$$\zeta' = \frac{\beta}{\alpha} = e' + if'.$$

(Note that e' and f' are not necessarily integers; but they are rational numbers. Hence ζ' is not necessarily a Gaussian integer. The division by α is possible since $\alpha \neq 0$.) Let e and f be the nearest integers to e' and f', respectively. Then clearly

$$|e - e'| \leqq \tfrac{1}{2}, \qquad |f - f'| \leqq \tfrac{1}{2}.$$

If $e = e'$, $f = f'$, then $\beta = \zeta'\alpha$, ζ' is a Gaussian integer and $\omega = 0$. This would complete our proof. Suppose, however, ζ' is *not* a Gaussian integer. Let $\zeta = e + if$ and let $\beta = \zeta\alpha + \omega$. Then $\omega = \beta - \zeta\alpha = (c + id) - (e + if)(a + ib)$ and

$$g(\omega) = g(\beta - \zeta\alpha) = g(\beta - \zeta'\alpha + (\zeta' - \zeta)\alpha) = g((\zeta' - \zeta)\alpha)$$
$$= g(\zeta' - \zeta)g(\alpha) \leqq [(\tfrac{1}{2})^2 + (\tfrac{1}{2})^2]g(\alpha) = \tfrac{1}{2}g(\alpha),$$

(the formula $g(\lambda\mu) = g(\lambda)g(\mu)$ holding even if λ and μ are "rational" complex numbers). Hence $g(\omega) \leqq \tfrac{1}{2}g(\alpha)$ and $g(\omega) < g(\alpha)$, which completes the proof.

2.13 Units and Primes

In an attempt to generalize certain phenomena that occur in simple rings such as the ring of integers Z or the ring of polynomials $\Delta[x]$ over the real field, we were led to certain abstract definitions in arbitrary rings. As we have remarked before, the motivation of such definitions is an attempt to generalize to abstract rings certain useful properties of concrete rings. One such definition led to Euclidean rings. Another important property of Z and $\Delta[x]$ is that of unique factorization. For example, we know that any integer can be factored into prime numbers, for example,

$$84 = 2^2 \cdot 3 \cdot 7. \tag{2.38}$$

In an attempt to generalize this important idea we shall define prime elements in general integral domains. It will turn out, as expected, that in the concrete ring Z the idea of a prime element coincides with that of a prime number. Also, after we have proved a few general theorems, the unique factorization of integers in Z as well as of polynomials in $\Delta[x]$ will be immediate corollaries.

Before making any definitions, let us look more closely at Equation 2.38. The factorization is not quite unique, that is, we could also write this equation as

$$84 = 2 \cdot 3 \cdot 2 \cdot 7.$$

However, this factorization differs from Equation 2.38 only in the order of the factors. Hence we shall be willing to say "factorization is unique up to the order of the elements." It would appear, therefore, that any reasonable definition should be restricted to commutative rings.

Another representation for Equation 2.38 is

$$84 = (-1)(-1)2^2 \cdot 3 \cdot 7(1)(1).$$

Again this is trivially different from Equation 2.38, since only plus and minus ones appear. So we would now be willing to say "factorization is unique up to the order of elements and plus and minus ones." However, there is one further point, namely,

$$84 = 2^2(-3)(-7).$$

We see that $-3 = (-1)3$, that is, -3 differs from 3 only by the factor -1.

To generalize these ideas we shall define *unit elements* in a ring. In the case of Z the only units will be $+1$ and -1. We shall also define *associated elements*. In the case of Z the only element associated with n will be its negative $-n$. Finally, we shall define *prime elements*. In the case of Z it will appear that the only prime elements are the prime numbers.

Based on this general definition we shall be able to prove that an element in a Euclidean ring without divisors of zero can be expressed uniquely (up to unit elements as factors and the order of the factors) as the product of prime elements (cf. Theorem 25). Since, for example, Z and $\Delta[x]$ are Euclidean rings without divisors of zero, we have immediately the unique factorization of integers and polynomials in a single variable over a field.

We now turn to the formal work of making precise the above qualitative remarks.

Definition. Let D be an integral domain. If ϵ is an element in D which possesses an inverse ϵ^{-1} in D, then we shall say ϵ is a *unit element*.

There may be more than one unit element in a ring. The reader should be sure that he does not confuse unit and unity. *The* unity element e in D has the property that $ea = a$ for all a in D. *A* unit ϵ has the property that ϵ^{-1} is in D and $\epsilon\epsilon^{-1} = e$. Clearly the *unity* element is a *unit*. In a field, every nonzero element is a unit. In the ring of integers Z the only units are $+1$ and -1. In the ring G of Gaussian integers $+1$, -1, $+i$, $-i$ are units. If ϵ is a unit element, then by the very definition of a unit, ϵ^{-1} is also a unit.

If two elements differ by a unit as a factor, they are called *associated elements*. That is, if a and b are elements of an integral domain D and $a = b\epsilon$ with ϵ a unit, then we call a and b *associated*. In Z, 3 and -3 are associated elements. In the ring of polynomials over the real field Δ, $x^3 - 3x$ and $2x^3 - 6x$ are associated elements since

$$x^3 - 3x = \tfrac{1}{2}(2x^3 - 6x)$$

and $\tfrac{1}{2}$ is a unit in Δ since $2(\tfrac{1}{2}) = 1$.

Since associated elements are closely related it is not surprising that they have similar properties. A theorem concerning associated elements that will be useful in further applications is the following.

Theorem 22. If D is an integral domain and (a) and (b) are two principal ideals in D distinct from the null ideal, then $(a) = (b)$ if and only if a and b are associated elements.

Proof: Suppose $(a) = (b)$. Since (a) is a principal ideal and D has a unity element, there exists an element r in D such that $a = rb$. Similarly, there exists an element s in D such that $b = sa$. From these two equations we conclude $a = rb = r(sa) = a(rs)$. By the definition of the additive inverse of $a(rs)$ and the distributivity of multiplication with respect to addition, we may write the last equation as $a(rs - 1) = 0$. Since D has no divisors of zero and $a \neq 0$, we conclude that $rs - 1 = 0$ or $rs = 1$. That is, r has an inverse and therefore r is a unit element. Since $a = rb$ we see that a and b are associated elements.

Conversely, suppose a and b are associated elements, $a = \epsilon b$ with ϵ a unit. Consider the principal ideals (a) and (b) generated by a and b, respectively. If c is any element in (a), then there exists an element r in D such that $c = ra$ (since D has a unity element). But $c = ra = r(\epsilon b) = (r\epsilon)b = r'b$, where $r' \in D$ and hence $c \in (b)$. Therefore we have shown that $(a) \subseteq (b)$. On the other hand, if d is an arbitrary element in (b), then $d = sb$ with s in D. But since ϵ is a unit, so is ϵ^{-1} and $b = \epsilon^{-1}a$. Therefore $d = sb = s(\epsilon^{-1}a) = (s\epsilon^{-1})a = s'a$ is an element in (a) and $(b) \subseteq (a)$. From the two relations $(a) \subseteq (b)$ and $(b) \subseteq (a)$ we see that $(a) = (b)$ as was desired to be proved.

A corollary may be drawn from the above proof. We note that in the proof of the fact that $(a) \subseteq (b)$ we did *not* use the fact that ϵ was a unit. In fact, if $a = bc$ with a, b, and c elements in an integral domain, then, by the same proof as above we can conclude that $(a) \subseteq (b)$.

Using the concept of units, we may sharpen some of our results on Euclidean rings. For example,

Theorem 23. Let R be a Euclidean ring free of divisors of zero. Let a and b be two nonzero elements in R. Then

(i) If b is a unit, $g(ab) = g(a)$.
(ii) If b is not a unit, $g(ab) > g(a)$.

Proof: By the very definition of a Euclidean ring,

$$g(ab) \geq g(a). \tag{2.39}$$

Now suppose that b is a unit. Then b^{-1} exists and

$$g(a) = g(b^{-1}(ba)) \geq g(ba) = g(ab). \tag{2.40}$$

From the two inequalities of Equations 2.39 and 2.40 we conclude that $g(ab) = g(a)$ with b a unit.

Suppose now that b is *not* a unit. Since $a \neq 0$, and R is a Euclidean ring, there exist elements q and r in R such that

$$a = q(ab) + r \tag{2.41}$$

where either $g(r) < g(ab)$ or $r = 0$. If $r = 0$, then $a = q(ab) = qb(a)$. Hence $(1 - qb)a = 0$. But R is an integral domain and $a \neq 0$. Hence $1 - qb = 0$ or $qb = 1$ and b must be a unit. This is a contradiction. Therefore

$$g(r) < g(ab). \tag{2.42}$$

From Equation 2.41 we may also write $r = a(1 - qb)$, and $g(r) = g(a(1 - qb)) \geq g(a)$. This equation and Equation 2.42 establish the fact that $g(ab) > g(a)$.

We are now in a position to define *prime elements* in arbitrary rings and prove some of their elementary properties. As expected, the idea of prime element coincides with that of prime number when the ring is specialized to the ring of integers Z.

Definition. Let $a = bc$ be a true equation in a ring R. Then the elements b and c are said to be *divisors* of a. An element p in an integral domain is said to be a *prime element* if its only divisors are units and elements associated with p.

If p is a prime element in an integral domain R, then from the equation $p = ab$ we can conclude that either a or b must be a unit. (If both a and b are units, then clearly so is p.) If $a = bc$ and b is *not* a unit, we shall call b a *proper* divisor of a. We see, for example, that in Z the number 7 is prime, since its only divisors are $1, -1, 7$, and -7. The numbers 1 and -1 are units and 7 and -7 are associated elements.

A convenient notation, which is also used in other branches of mathematics is $p|a$. This is read "p divides a." Similarly $p \nmid a$ means "p does not divide a."

Theorem 24. Let R be a principal ideal ring which is also an integral domain. Let p be a prime element in R which divides the product ab, where a and b are also in R. Then either p divides a or p divides b (or both).

Proof: If p or b is a unit, the theorem is trivial. Suppose, then that neither p nor b is a unit. If p divides b, our theorem is proved. Let us therefore assume that p does not divide b. We shall prove that p must divide a.

Consider the ideal (p,b) generated by p and b. Since R is a p.i.r., there exists an element d in R such that

$$(d) = (p,b). \tag{2.43}$$

Hence $p = rd$, $r \in R$ since R is commutative with unity. Since p is a prime element by hypothesis, either r or d must be a unit. Suppose r is a unit. Then p and d are associated elements and by Theorem 22 they generate the same principal ideal, that is,

$$(p) = (d). \tag{2.44}$$

Hence from Equations 2.43 and 2.44,

$$b = sd = tp, \qquad s \in R, \qquad t \in R,$$

and p divides b. This contradicts our assumption that $p \nmid b$.

The other alternative is that d is a unit. Thus $(d) = (e) = R$ since d^{-1} exists and $e = d^{-1}d$ is an element of (d). But $(d) = (p,b)$. Hence

$R = (p,b)$. Every element of R can be expressed as the sum of a ring multiple of p and a ring multiple of b. In particular e has this property, that is, there exist two ring elements u and v such that

$$e = up + vb. \tag{2.45}$$

But, on multiplying by a,

$$ae = a = aup + v(ab).$$

By hypothesis $p|ab$. Clearly $p|p$. Therefore $p|a$.

As a corollary to this theorem we can state that if a prime element p divides the product $a_1a_2 \cdots a_n$, then p divides some a_j.

Interpreted in terms of integers (the ring Z) our theorem states that if a prime number divides the product of two integers, it must divide one or the other (or both) of these integers.

If R is an integral domain with the property that every nonzero element in R can be expressed uniquely (up to unit elements as factors and the order of the factors) as the product of prime elements—then we shall say that the *unique factorization theorem* holds in R. For example, we have the following important theorem.

Theorem 25. Let R be a Euclidean ring which is also an integral domain. Then the unique factorization theorem holds in R.

Proof: Suppose a is a nonzero element in R and $g(a) = 0$. Let $a = bc$ with c not a unit. By Theorem 23 $g(a) > g(b)$. This is impossible since the g function of a Euclidean ring is nonnegative. Hence c must be a unit and a must be a prime element.

The theorem will now be proved by complete induction on the integers $g(a)$. Assume the theorem is true for all elements $b \in R$ with $g(b) < n$, and let $g(a) = n$. If a is a prime element, then the theorem is clearly true. Suppose a is not prime. Then a has a (not necessarily unique) representation $a = bc$, where b and c are both proper divisors of a. By Theorem 23, $g(b) < g(a)$, $g(c) < g(a)$, and by the induction hypothesis, b and c can be uniquely expressed as the product of prime elements. This does not quite prove uniqueness, for we could have written $a = \beta\gamma$ and applied the same reasoning to β and γ as we did to b and c. So while the factorizations of β and γ would be unique, we could not conclude that the factorization of a was unique.

Suppose then

$$a = p_1p_2 \cdots p_r \quad \text{and} \quad a = q_1q_2 \cdots q_s, \tag{2.46}$$

where no p_j or q_k is a unit, are two factorizations of a into prime elements. Since a Euclidean ring is a p.i.r., Theorem 24 applies, and hence p_1 must divide some q_k, $k = 1, 2, \cdots, s$, say $p_1 | q_{k_1}$. Hence

$$q_{k_1} = \epsilon_1 p_1. \tag{2.47}$$

The element ϵ_1 in the above equation must be a unit, for if it were not, q_{k_1} would not be prime. Using this result in Equation 2.46, we may write, by the commutativity of R and the distributivity of multiplication with respect to addition,

$$0 = a - a = p_1 p_2 \cdots p_r - q_{k_1} q_{k_2} \cdots q_{k_s}$$
$$= p_1 p_2 \cdots p_r - \epsilon_1 p_1 q_{k_2} \cdots q_{k_s} = p_1(p_2 \cdots p_r - \epsilon_1 q_{k_2} \cdots q_{k_s}) = 0.$$

Since R is an integral domain and $p_1 \neq 0$, we must have

$$p_2 \cdots p_r = \epsilon_1 q_{k_2} \cdots q_{k_s}.$$

Now by Theorem 23,

$$g(a) = g(p_1 p_2 \cdots p_r) > g(p_2 \cdots p_r)$$
$$g(a) = g(q_1 q_2 \cdots q_s) > g(q_{k_2} \cdots q_{k_s}) = g(\epsilon_1 q_{k_2} \cdots q_{k_s}).$$

By the induction hypothesis, $p_2 \cdots p_r = \epsilon_1 q_{k_2} \cdots q_{k_s}$ must differ only by unit elements and the order of the factors. Hence, by suitably rearranging the q_k terms, we may write

$$q_{k_j} = \epsilon_j p_j, \qquad j = 2, \cdots, r,$$

where ϵ_j is a unit. In particular, $r = s$. Together with Equation 2.47, this proves the theorem.

An immediate corollary to this theorem is that the unique factorization theorem holds in Z. Also, if Δ is a field, then Δ and $\Delta[x]$ are Euclidean rings free of divisors of zero. Hence Theorem 25 applies and the unique factorization theorem holds in Δ and $\Delta[x]$.

For example, let Δ be the field of rational numbers and let

$$f(x) = x^4 - 6x^2 - 7x - 6$$

be an element in $\Delta[x]$. Then we may write

$$f(x) = (x^2 + x + 1)(x - 3)(x + 2)$$

using high school algebra. The factors $x - 3$ and $x + 2$ are prime. The factor $x^2 + x + 1$ is also prime, since the equation

$$x^2 + x + 1 = (x - \alpha)(x - \beta)$$

is impossible with α and β rational numbers. By the theorem just proved, this factorization is unique up to units and the order of the factors, for example,

$$f(x) = 3(\tfrac{1}{4})(-\tfrac{1}{3})(x - 3)(-4)(x^2 + x + 1)(x + 2).$$

In an earlier section we defined a *prime ideal* as an ideal N which had the property that $ab \in N$ implied a or b in N. Recently we defined a *prime element*. The relation between these two concepts is expressed in the following theorem.

Theorem 26. Let R be an integral domain in which the unique factorization theorem holds. Then every prime element in R generates a prime ideal.

Proof: Let p be a prime element in R and let (p) be the ideal generated by p. We shall show that (p) is prime. If p is a unit, the theorem is trivial. Assume, then, that p is not a unit.

Suppose ab is an element of (p);

$$ab \equiv 0 \quad (p).*$$

Since the unique factorization theorem holds in R, ab can be expressed as the product of prime elements in R, namely,

$$ab = p_1 p_2 \cdots p_n.$$

But p divides ab, and since the unique factorization theorem holds in R, p must divide some p_i. Hence $p = \epsilon p_i$. Since p is prime, ϵ must be a unit.

In the factorization of ab, p_i must appear in either a or b (or both). Hence $p|a$ or $p|b$. Thus either $a \equiv 0 \quad (p)$ or $b \equiv 0 \quad (p)$. This establishes the fact that (p) is a prime ideal.

As a matter of notation we note that the following four statements are equivalent:

(i) $\alpha \in (p)$

(ii) $\alpha \equiv 0 \quad (p)$

(iii) $p|\alpha$

(iv) $\alpha = rp, \quad r \in R,$

where (p) is a principal ideal in any commutative ring R with a unity element. Which form we use is strictly a matter of convenience.

---

* Strictly speaking we should write $ab \equiv 0 \ ((p))$. However, it is customary to drop one set of parentheses.

As a corollary to Theorem 26 we can show that every nonprime element distinct from zero in R generates a nonprime ideal.

As an application of Theorem 26 we see immediately that the ideal (29) is prime in Z and that $(x^2 + 1)$ is a prime ideal in $\Delta[x]$, where Δ is the field of real or rational numbers. However, in the field of complex numbers K, $(x^2 + 1)$ is not a prime ideal in $K[x]$, since $x^2 + 1 = (x + i)(x - i)$ is not a prime element in $K[x]$.

Before proving our general theorem on the unique factorization of elements in polynomial domains, Theorem 28, we shall prove an interesting theorem which is a generalization of the familiar Euclidean algorithm of elementary algebra. We define, first, the concept of a *greatest common divisor* in an arbitrary Euclidean ring.

Definition. Let E be a Euclidean ring and let $a \neq 0$ and b be two elements of E. Let d be an element of E which divides both a and b. If all other common divisors δ of a and b have the property that $g(\delta) \leq g(d)$, then we shall call d a *greatest common divisor* (G.C.D.) of a and b.

If $E = Z$, then the G.C.D. of any two integers has the significance attributed to it in elementary algebra and is unique except for associated elements [since $g(m) = g(n)$ implies $|m| = |n|$ or $m = \pm n$]. In a field Δ every nonzero element d in Δ is a G.C.D. of any two elements α and β in Δ, since $g(d) = g(\alpha) = g(\beta) = 0$.

The Euclidean algorithm is as follows.

Theorem 27. Let E be a Euclidean ring which is also an integral domain and let $a \neq 0$ and b be two elements in E. Let d be a greatest common divisor of a and b. Then there exist elements α and β in E such that

$$d = \alpha a + \beta b.$$

Proof: By definition of a Euclidean ring we know that there exist elements q_1 and r_1 in E such that $b = q_1 a + r_1$ where either $g(r_1) < g(a)$ or else $r_1 = 0$.

If $r_1 = 0$, then our theorem is true with a a greatest common divisor. Suppose, $r_1 \neq 0$. Then we may apply the division algorithm to r_1 and a, obtaining $a = q_2 r_1 + r_2$, where either $g(r_2) < g(r_1)$ or $r_2 = 0$.

Proceeding in this fashion we shall reach, in a finite number of steps, an r_{k+1} which is zero. This must be the case since

$$g(r_1) > g(r_2) > \cdots > g(r_k)$$

is a decreasing sequence of nonnegative integers.   Hence we may write

$$b = q_1 a + r_1$$
$$a = q_2 r_1 + r_2$$
$$r_1 = q_3 r_2 + r_3 \qquad\qquad (2.48)$$
$$. \quad . \quad . \quad . \quad . \quad .$$
$$r_{k-2} = q_k r_{k-1} + r_k$$
$$r_{k-1} = q_{k+1} r_k + 0.$$

We assert that r_k is a G.C.D. of a and b.   For, from the last of the above equations we conclude that $r_k | r_{k-1}$.   From the next to the last equation, we conclude that $r_k | r_{k-2}$.   Continuing in this fashion we see that $r_k | r_{k-3}$, etc., and finally that r_k divides a and b.   Hence r_k *is a divisor* of a and b.   Now suppose that δ is *any* divisor of a and b.   We shall show that $\delta | r_k$.   For, from the first of the above equations we conclude that $\delta | r_1$.   From the second, we conclude that $\delta | r_2$.   Proceeding in this fashion, we see finally that $\delta | r_k$.   Hence $r_k = \delta c$, where $c \in E$. But from the definition of a Euclidean ring, $g(r_k) \geq g(\delta)$.   Hence by our definition of G.C.D., r_k is a greatest common divisor of a and b.

To obtain the representation for a G.C.D. stated in the theorem, replace r_{k-1} and r_{k-2} in the next to the last of Equations 2.48 by $r_{k-3} - q_{k-1} r_{k-2} = r_{k-1}$ and $r_{k-4} - q_{k-2} r_{k-3} = r_{k-2}$, respectively, obtaining

$$[r_{k-4} - q_{k-2} r_{k-3}] - q_k[r_{k-3} - q_{k-1} r_{k-2}] = r_k.$$

Continuing this process, we can replace r_{k-2}, r_{k-3}, and r_{k-4} on the left-hand side of the above equation until we reach a and b.   We shall then have the desired relation

$$r_k = a\alpha + \beta b$$

where α and β are products and sums of element in E.

The above theorem gives us an actual construction (hence the term "algorithm") which may be used in finding the G.C.D. d of two elements a and b as well as the elements α and β such that $d = \alpha a + \beta b$.   For example, let $E = Z$ and let $a = 754, b = 46$.   Then

$$46 = 0 \cdot 754 + 46$$
$$754 = 16 \cdot 46 + 18$$
$$46 = 2 \cdot 18 + 10$$
$$18 = 1 \cdot 10 + 8$$
$$10 = 1 \cdot 8 + 2$$
$$8 = 4 \cdot 2 + 0.$$

Hence a G.C.D. of 754 and 46 is 2. Furthermore, substituting back in the above equations

$$(46 - 2 \cdot 18) - 1 \cdot (18 - 1 \cdot 10) = 2$$
$$46 - 3 \cdot 18 + 10 = 2$$
$$46 - 3[754 - 16 \cdot 46] + [46 - 2(754 - 16 \cdot 46)] = 2$$
$$2 = (-5)(754) + (82)(46)$$

which is the desired relation. Therefore, by a relatively simple method we have determined not only a G.C.D. but the numbers $\alpha = -5$ and $\beta = 82$ as well.

If in particular, a and b are relatively prime, that is, the only common divisors of a and b are units, then we have the important relation

$$1 = \alpha a + \beta b.$$

One can use the formula to prove such theorems as: If a and b are relatively prime integers (in Z) and a divides the product bc (where c is also in Z), then a must divide c. To prove this, we multiply the above equation by c, $c = (\alpha c)a + \beta(bc)$. Since $a|a$, $a|bc$, we must have $a|c$. Another argument using this same idea appeared in Equation 2.45 of Theorem 24.

One could, of course, consider the ring of polynomials $\Delta[x]$ over a field Δ and apply Theorem 27 to find a G.C.D. of two polynomials. (Cf. the exercises at the end of this chapter.)

2.14 Unique Factorization Theorem

In Theorem 25 we proved that in a Euclidean ring without divisors of zero every nonzero element could be uniquely expressed as the product of prime elements. An immediate corollary was the fact that the unique factorization theorem held in the polynomial domain $\Delta[x]$, where Δ was a field. However, the ring $\Delta[x,y]$ is not a Euclidean ring (in fact, it is not even a p.i.r.). Hence we cannot appeal to Theorem 25 in an effort to prove that the unique factorization theorem holds in $\Delta[x,y]$. But from elementary algebra we know that the unique factorization of polynomials in two variables *does* hold. In the present section we shall obtain this result as a corollary to the general unique factorization theorem (cf. Theorem 28).

A preliminary definition that will be convenient in the proof of the theorem is the notion of a *primitive polynomial*.

Definition. Let $D[x]$ be the ring of polynomials over an integral domain D. If the coefficients of a polynomial $f(x)$ in $D[x]$ have no common divisors except units, then $f(x)$ will be called a *primitive polynomial*.

For example, $f(x) = 3x^2 - 4x + 35$ is a primitive polynomial in $Z[x]$. In the ring of polynomials over a field, every polynomial is primitive.

With these preliminary remarks we can now state and prove the fundamental theorem regarding factorizations in polynomial domains. In what follows we shall frequently use the term "irreducible polynomial" to describe a prime element in a polynomial domain. Such terminology is in harmony with the definitions made in elementary algebra.

Theorem 28. Let D be an integral domain in which the unique factorization theorem holds. Then the unique factorization theorem holds in the ring of polynomials $D[x]$ over D.

Proof: We shall first prove that the product of primitive polynomials is primitive. Suppose that

$$\phi(x) = a_0 + a_1 x + \cdots, \qquad a_i \in D$$

and

$$\psi(x) = b_0 + b_1 x + \cdots, \qquad b_j \in D$$

are two primitive polynomials in $D[x]$. We shall show that their product

$$\chi(x) = \phi(x)\psi(x) = c_0 + c_1 x + \cdots, \qquad c_k \in D$$

is also primitive. To prove this statement we shall suppose that $\chi(x)$ is not primitive. If this be the case, then there exists an element α in D which divides every c_i, and further α is not a unit. Let p be any prime factor of α. Such a p must exist, since the unique factorization theorem holds in D.

Suppose that p divides a_i, $i = 0, 1, \cdots, r - 1$ but that p does not divide a_r. There must exist such an a_r since otherwise p would divide every a_i and $\phi(x)$ would not be primitive—which contradicts the hypothesis. Similarly, let $p \mid b_i$, $i = 0, 1, \cdots, s - 1$ but not divide b_s. Now consider the coefficient c_{r+s} of x^{r+s} in the expression for $\chi(x)$. By definition of multiplication of polynomials it is

$$c_{r+s} = a_0 b_{r+s} + a_1 b_{r+s-1} + \cdots + a_{r-1} b_{s+1} + a_r b_s +$$
$$+ a_{r+1} b_{s-1} + \cdots + a_{r+s} b_0.$$

Since $p \mid a_i$, $i = 0, 1, \cdots, r - 1$ and $p \mid b_j$, $j = 0, 1, \cdots, s - 1$, every term on the right-hand side of the above expression except possibly $a_r b_s$ must be divisible by p. But $p \mid c_{r+s}$ since p divides every c_k. Hence p must divide $a_r b_s$. Since the unique factorization theorem holds in D, and p divides $a_r b_s$, the element p must occur in either the factorization of a_r or b_s (or both). Hence $p \mid a_r$ or $p \mid b_s$, which contradicts the assumption that $p \nmid a_r$ and $p \nmid b_s$. Hence $\chi(x) = \phi(x)\psi(x)$ is a primitive polynomial. (The result that the product of two primitive polynomials is a primitive polynomial is frequently called "Gauss's lemma.")

Suppose now that $f(x)$ is an arbitrary element in $D[x]$. We wish to show that it has a unique factorization as the product of prime elements in $D[x]$. We start by considering the *quotient field* Δ of D (cf. Section 2.5). Certainly $f(x)$ is an element of $\Delta[x]$. By the corollary to Theorem 25, $f(x)$ can be uniquely factored into prime elements in $\Delta[x]$, say

$$f(x) = F_1(x) F_2(x) \cdots F_r(x), \qquad F_i(x) \in \Delta[x].$$

Now if $G(x)$ is any polynomial in $\Delta[x]$ we may write $G(x) = \dfrac{1}{d} g(x)$,

where $g(x)$ is in $D[x]$ and d is a nonzero element in D, that is, $d \in D - \{0\}$. Also we may write $g(x) = c\psi(x)$, where c is an element in D and $\psi(x)$ is a *primitive* polynomial in $D[x]$. Hence every element $G(x)$ in $\Delta[x]$ may be written in the form $G(x) = \dfrac{c}{d}\psi(x)$, where $c \in D$, $d \in D - \{0\}$, and $\psi(x)$ is a primitive polynomial in $D[x]$.

In particular,

$$F_i(x) = \frac{a_i}{b_i}\phi_i(x) \tag{2.49}$$

and

$$f(x) = \frac{a_1 a_2 \cdots a_r}{b_1 b_2 \cdots b_r} \phi_1(x)\phi_2(x) \cdots \phi_r(x)$$

or

$$f(x) = \frac{a}{b}\phi_1(x)\phi_2(x) \cdots \phi_r(x) \tag{2.50}$$

where $a = a_1 a_2 \cdots a_r$ and $b = b_1 b_2 \cdots b_r$ are units in Δ and the $\phi_i(x)$ are primitive polynomials in $D[x]$.

We may also write (in $D[x]$), $f(x) = \alpha\phi(x)$, where $\alpha \in D$ and $\phi(x)$ is primitive in $D[x]$. Comparing this with Equation 2.50 and noting that $\phi_1 \phi_2 \cdots \phi_r$ is primitive, we conclude that b is a unit in D.

The $\phi_i(x)$ are irreducible polynomials in $D[x]$. For suppose they were not. That is, suppose $\phi_i(x) = \lambda_i(x)\mu_i(x)$, where neither λ_i nor μ_i is a unit. Since ϕ_i is primitive, neither λ_i nor μ_i can be an element in D. Therefore from Equation 2.49 we would have

$$F_i(x) = \frac{a_i}{b_i}\lambda_i(x)\mu_i(x)$$

in $\Delta[x]$ which contradicts the fact that $F_i(x)$ is prime.

Also, because of the unique factorization in D we may write $a = p_1 p_2 \cdots p_h$ uniquely where the p_i are prime elements in D. Hence $f(x) = p_1 p_2 \cdots p_h \phi_1(x) \phi_2(x) \cdots \phi_r(x)$ is a representation of $f(x)$ in terms of prime elements in $D[x]$.

This representation is unique. For suppose $f(x)$ also equaled

$$q_1 q_2 \cdots q_k \psi_1(x) \psi_2(x) \cdots \psi_s(x). \tag{2.51}$$

Since the ϕ and ψ are primitive and the factorization in D is unique, we must have $p_i = \epsilon_i q_{j_i}$, $i = 1, 2, \cdots, h$, where the ϵ_i are units in D. In particular $h = k$. Furthermore, since the factorization of Equation 2.51 holds in $\varDelta[x]$ also, we must have (because of the unique factorization in $\varDelta[x]$) that $\phi_i = \delta_i \psi_{j_i}$, $i = 1, 2, \cdots, r$ where the δ_i are units in $\varDelta$. But ϕ_i and ψ_{j_i} are primitive. Hence δ_i is also a unit in D. This completes the proof of the theorem.

Since $\varDelta[x]$ (where $\varDelta$ is a field) is also an integral domain in which the unique factorization theorem holds, the theorem must hold in $\varDelta[x,y]$. Similarly, by complete induction, we can obtain the unique factorization of polynomials in n indeterminates over a field $\varDelta$. (Cf. Theorem 15.)

Another corollary that can be drawn from the proof of the above theorem is: If a primitive polynomial cannot be factored in an integral domain $D[x]$, it cannot be factored in $\varDelta[x]$, where $\varDelta$ is the field of quotients of D.

We have defined the greatest common divisor of two elements in a Euclidean ring. However, certain important rings, for example, the ring of polynomials in two variables over a field $\varDelta$, are not Euclidean rings. Nevertheless we can still define the concept of G.C.D. in an integral domain in which the unique factorization theorem holds.

Let, then, D be an integral domain in which unique factorization theorem holds. Then if ϕ and ψ are two elements in D we can express ϕ and ψ as the product of prime elements in D, viz.:

$$\phi = a_1 a_2 \cdots a_r, \qquad a_i \in D$$
$$\psi = b_1 b_2 \cdots b_s, \qquad b_j \in D$$

and these representations are unique up to unit elements as factors. It may be, by suitably rearranging the factors, that $a_i = \epsilon_i b_i$, $i = 1, 2, \cdots, t$, where t is less than or equal to the minimum of r and s, and the ϵ_i are units in D; and no other a_j is equal to a unit times any other b_k, $j = t + 1, \cdots, r$; $k = t + 1, \cdots, s$. We shall call

$$d = a_1 a_2 \cdots a_t$$

a *greatest common divisor* of ϕ and ψ.

If D also happens to be a Euclidean ring, we see that this definition coincides with the definition of G.C.D. given for Euclidean rings.

2.15 Zeros of a Polynomial

An important topic considered in elementary algebra was that of determining the roots of an algebraic equation. If $f(x)$ was a polynomial, then we sought a number α such that $f(\alpha) = 0$. Such a number was called a *root* of the equation. It was stated (with or without proof) that every algebraic equation of the n *th* degree had n roots. The difficult part of this theorem, of course, was to prove the existence of at least *one* root.

These concepts, when suitably phrased in abstract terms, lead to important results in abstract field theory which will be considered in the next chapter. To make the above notion precise, let us start by considering the ring of polynomials $Z[x]$. If $f(x) = x^2 - 5x + 6$ is an element in $Z[x]$, then clearly, if we replace x by any integer α we obtain another element of $Z : f(\alpha) = \alpha^2 - 5\alpha + 6$, where α^2 is to be interpreted as "α times α." In particular $f(2) = 0$ and $f(3) = 0$. Hence the elements 2 and 3 of Z will be called *roots* of $f(x) = 0$.

However, consider the polynomial $g(x) = x^2 - 2$ in $Z[x]$. Of course, it has the property that $g(\alpha) = \alpha^2 - 2$ is an integer for any $\alpha \in Z$. But there exists no element β *in* Z such that $g(\beta) \equiv 0$. One might argue that $\pm \sqrt{2}$ satisfies this condition, but $\sqrt{2}$ is *not* an element in Z. We are therefore forced to say that $x^2 - 2$ has no zeros *in* Z. If, however, we consider $x^2 - 2$ as a polynomial in $\varDelta[x]$, where $\varDelta$ is the field of real numbers, then it *does* have a zero in $\varDelta$. Our main difficulty, then, in stating that a certain element α makes a polynomial vanish is in determining from what admissible set we are willing to select α.

With the above illustration in mind we are led to the following definitions, which will establish a firm basis for the treatment of our theory.

Definition. Let R be a given ring. Let S be another ring which contains R. Then we shall call S a *superring* over R.

Clearly, then, R is a subring of S. The field of rational numbers is a superring with respect to the integers; the field of real numbers is a superring with respect to the rational numbers, the field of complex numbers is a superring with respect to the real numbers. In these examples, we could, of course, have used the term *superfield* instead of superring.

Returning for a moment to the example $g(x) = x^2 - 2$ in $Z[x]$, we see that $g(x)$ has no zeros in Z. However, if we consider the superring $\varDelta$ of real numbers, then $g(x)$ considered as a polynomial in $\varDelta[x]$ has a zero in $\varDelta$. For the purposes of the present section it will suffice to assume that any zeros of a given polynomial in a ring $R[x]$ lie in R. (In the next chapter we shall consider in greater detail the structure of superfields.)

We have yet to define the zero of a polynomial in the general case.

Definition. Let R be a commutative ring and let $f(x)$ be an element in $R[x]$. If α is an element in R with the property that $f(\alpha) = 0$, then we shall call α a *zero* of the polynomial $f(x)$ or a *root* of the equation $f(x) = 0$.

From the example considered above we see that in a given ring R there may be no elements in R which are zeros of a given polynomial in $R[x]$.

After these preliminary remarks we can now prove, in abstract terms, a familiar theorem of elementary algebra.

Theorem 29. Let $\varDelta$ be a field and $f(x)$ an element in $\varDelta[x]$. Let $\alpha \in \varDelta$ be a zero of $f(x)$. Then $x - \alpha$ divides $f(x)$.

Proof: By Theorem 20, $\varDelta[x]$ is a Euclidean ring. Hence we may apply the division algorithm to $f(x)$ and $x - \alpha$, obtaining

$$f(x) = q(x)(x - \alpha) + r(x),$$

where $q(x)$ and $r(x)$ are elements of $\varDelta[x]$ and either the degree of $r(x)$ is less than that of $x - \alpha$ (that is, it is zero) or else $r(x)$ is identically zero. In either case, $r \in \varDelta$. Now replace x by α in the above expression. Then

$$0 = f(\alpha) = q(\alpha)(\alpha - \alpha) + r = r$$

and $f(x) = q(x)(x - \alpha)$. Hence, by the very definition of divisor, $x - \alpha$ divides $f(x)$.

Under the hypothesis of Theorem 29 let β be any element in $\varDelta$. Then applying the division algorithm to $f(x)$ and $x - \beta$ we obtain $f(x) = q(x)(x - \beta) + s$, where $s \in \varDelta$. Letting $x = \beta$, we have $f(\beta) = s$. This result is known as the *remainder theorem*. Actually, Theorem 29 is a corollary, for if β is a zero of $f(x)$, then $f(\beta) = 0$ and hence $s = 0$.

In investigating the zeros of a polynomial, a convenient tool (borrowed from the calculus) is the notion of the *derivative* of a polynomial. Since, so far, we have no limiting processes in our algebraic theory, we lay down the following definition for a polynomial calculus.

Definition.   Let R be a commutative ring and let $f(x) = \sum_{k=0}^{n} a_k x^k$
be an element in $R[x]$.   Then we define the *derivative* $f'(x)$ of $f(x)$ as the
polynomial

$$f'(x) = \sum_{k=1}^{n} k a_k x^{k-1}.$$

Clearly $f'(x)$ is also an element of $R[x]$.

On the basis of this definition we can prove the familiar formulas
$(f + g)' = f' + g'$ and $(fg)' = f'g + fg'$.

We use the word "derivative" because of the form of $f'(x)$ as used
in analysis.   However, from our abstract point of view, putting a
"prime" on a polynomial is simply a technique for generating a new
polynomial from a given polynomial.   If the reader were not familiar
with the calculus it would appear as a rather strange definition.   However, from our knowledge of this branch of analysis, we do not need any
motivation to be convinced that this concept will yield fruitful results.

If Δ is a field and $x - \alpha$ is a factor of $f(x) \in \Delta[x]$ where $\alpha \in \Delta$ then
we saw that $(x - \alpha) | f(x)$.   Now it may be that $(x - \alpha)^2$ also divides
$f(x)$.   In this case we say that α is a *double* root of $f(x) = 0$, and more
generally,

Definition.   If R is an integral domain, $f(x)$ a polynomial in $R[x]$,
and $\alpha \in R$ a root of $f(x)$ such that $(x - \alpha)^k | f(x)$, but $(x - \alpha)^{k+1} \nmid f(x)$,
then we call α a zero of *multiplicity* k.   In particular, if $k = 1$, we shall
say that α is a *simple zero*.

With this definition and our definition of derivative of a polynomial
we may prove the following theorem.

Theorem 30.   If Δ is a field and $f(x) \in \Delta[x]$ has a zero α of multiplicity k, then $f'(x)$ has α as a zero of multiplicity at least $k - 1$.

Proof: Suppose that $\alpha \in \Delta$ is a zero of $f(x)$ of multiplicity k.   Then
$f(x) = p(x)(x - \alpha)^k$, where $p(x) \in \Delta[x]$ and $(x - \alpha) \nmid p(x)$.   [For if
$(x - \alpha) | p(x)$, then $(x - \alpha)^{k+1}$ would divide $f(x)$—which contradicts the
assumption that α is a zero of multiplicity k.]   Now, from the definition
of derivative,

$$f'(x) = p'(x)(x - \alpha)^k + k p(x)(x - \alpha)^{k-1}. \qquad (2.52)$$

Clearly $(x - \alpha)^{k-1}$ divides the right-hand side of the above expression.
Hence $(x - \alpha)^{k-1} | f'(x)$ and α is a zero of multiplicity at least $k - 1$.

Using the same techniques we can show that a polynomial of
degree n has at most n zeros in a field Δ, (cf. the exercises at the end
of this chapter).   An immediate corollary of this remark is

Theorem 31. If $f(x)$ is an element in $\Delta[x]$ of degree n and the field Δ contains more than n elements, then there exists an element α in Δ such that $f(\alpha) \neq 0$.

The peculiar remark "the field Δ contains more than n elements" in the above theorem may at first surprise the reader. When one thinks of "field" one has in mind such fields as the fields of real and complex numbers which contain an infinite number of elements. However, fields have been defined abstractly and there is no reason to suppose that they may not have only a finite number of elements (cf. Theorem 5). In fact we shall intensively study the properties of "finite fields" in the next chapter. Also because of the existence of such pathological fields we cannot strengthen Theorem 30 to read " α is a zero of multiplicity exactly $k - 1$ of $f'(x)$." In fields "of characteristic zero" (cf. page 128) this stronger form of Theorem 30 *is* true.

With our present knowledge of ideal theory, we can even construct some simple finite fields, (cf. the exercises at the end of this chapter). For example, let Z be the ring of integers and let p be a prime element (number) in Z. Let (p) be the principal ideal generated by p. Then the ring of remainder classes $Z/(p)$ contains p elements, say

$$\{\bar{0},\ \bar{1},\ \bar{2},\ \cdots \overline{p-1}\}.$$

(Cf. Exercise 2.3 at the end of this chapter. Under the natural homomorphism $\nu: Z \to Z/(p)$, an element α in Z is mapped on the residue class $\alpha + (p)$. Call this residue class $\bar{\alpha}$.) By Theorems 26, 12, and 5, we conclude that $Z/(p)$ is a field.

In the next paragraph we shall use this field as an example to prove the statement "if a polynomial vanishes for all elements of a field, it is identically zero" is *not* necessarily true. This statement is quoted as a true statement in elementary algebra, that is, the identical vanishing of a polynomial for all elements is considered equivalent to the statement that a polynomial is identically zero. We hasten to add that this statement *is* true in fields which contain an infinite number of elements (the only ones used in elementary algebra) but it is not necessarily true in finite fields (cf. the previous theorem). Since in abstract algebra we are dealing with a general field, we do not know a priori whether it is finite or not and hence, in general, we cannot conclude that the two statements "a polynomial vanishes identically for all elements in the field" and "a polynomial is identically zero" are equivalent statements.

Consider the polynomial $f(x) = x^p - x$ in $Z/(p)[x]$. This polynomial is certainly not identically zero. The elements $\bar{1}, \bar{2}, \cdots, \overline{p-1}$ of $Z/(p)$ form a cyclic group of order $p - 1$, (cf. Exercise 1.4 of

Chapter 1).   Hence $\bar{\alpha}^{p-1} = \bar{1}$ for all $\bar{\alpha}$ in $Z/(p)$, and also $\bar{\alpha}^p - \bar{\alpha} = \bar{0}$ for all $\bar{\alpha}$ in $Z/(p)$.   Clearly $\bar{0}^p - \bar{0} = \bar{0}$ and hence $f(x) = x^p - x$ vanishes identically for all $\bar{\alpha} \in Z/(p)$.

2.16 The Hilbert Basis Theorem

As a final application of ideal theory proper, before we pass on to an intensive study of field theory, we shall prove an interesting theorem known as the Hilbert basis theorem.   Certain of the ideas contained in this theorem are useful in the theory of algebraic numbers.

We shall say that a commutative ring R has the *basis property* if every ideal in R is generated by a finite number of elements of R. (Such rings are also called *Noetherian rings*.)   That is, if N is an ideal in R, then $N = (a_1, a_2, \cdots, a_s)$, where $a_i \in R$.   (A p.i.r. has the basis property since every ideal in a p.i.r. is generated by a single element.) Every element in N can therefore be expressed in the form

$$r_1 a_1 + \cdots + r_s a_s + n_1 a_1 + \cdots + n_s a_s,$$

where $r_i \in R$ and the n_i are integers (in Z).   If R has a unity element, the terms involving n_i can be deleted from the above expression.   The set of elements $\{a_1, a_2, \cdots, a_s\}$ used above is called a *basis*, in particular, a finite *basis*.

If R is an arbitrary ring and $N_j, j = 1, 2, \cdots$ is a finite or infinite set of ideals in R which have the property that $N_j \subseteq N_{j+1}, j = 1, 2, \cdots$; then we shall call the $\{N_j\}$ a *chain of ideals* in R.   Suppose, then, that $\{N_i\}$ is a chain of ideals in a ring R such that either

(i) Each N_i is properly contained in N_{i+1}, that is, $N_i \subset N_{i+1}$ and the chain has only a finite number of ideals, or

(ii) The chain is infinite with $N_i \subseteq N_{i+1}$ and after a certain integer n, all terms are equal; $N_n = N_{n+1} = N_{n+2} = \cdots$.

If this be the case, we shall say that R has the *chain of divisors property*. Of course these two statements are equivalent.

Our first theorem will be to show that these two definitions are coextensive.

Theorem 32.   If a ring R has the basis property, then it has the chain of divisors property and conversely.

Proof: (a) The basis property implies the chain of divisors property.

Let $N_1, N_2, \cdots$ be an infinite chain of ideals in R with $N_i \subseteq N_{i+1}$. Let N be the set of all elements belonging to at least one ideal N_i. We assert that N is an ideal.   For suppose a and b are elements in N. Then a is in some N_n (and all other N_p with $p > n$) and b is in some

N_m (and all other N_q with $q > m$). Let β be the larger of the two integers n and m. Then a and b are both in N_β. Since N_β is an ideal, $a + b$, ab, ra, ar' (with r and r' in R) are in N_β and hence in N. We see therefore that N is an ideal. By the basis property there exists a finite number of elements $a_1, a_2, \cdots, a_s$ in R which generate N, that is $N = (a_1, a_2, \cdots, a_s)$. Suppose that $a_i \in N_{n_i}$ and let α be the maximum of the integers $n_1, n_2, \cdots, n_s$. Then $N \subseteq N_\alpha$. But $N_\alpha \subseteq N$. We conclude therefore that

$$N = N_\alpha = N_{\alpha+1} = \cdots$$

and R has the chain of divisors property.

(b) The chain of divisors property implies the basis property.

We must show that every ideal N in R has a finite basis. Let N be an ideal in R and let a_1 be an element of N. If a_1 does not generate the entire ideal, then there exists an element a_2 in N which is not in (a_1). Hence $(a_1) \subset (a_1, a_2)$. If a_1 and a_2 do not generate N there exists a third element a_3 in N which is not in (a_1, a_2) such that $(a_1) \subset (a_1, a_2) \subset (a_1, a_2, a_3)$. Continuing in this fashion we obtain a chain of ideals,

$$(a_1) \subset (a_1, a_2) \subset (a_1, a_2, a_3) \cdots$$

But by the chain of divisors property, there exists only a finite number of these ideals, say s. Hence $N = (a_1, a_2, \cdots, a_s)$ and N has a finite basis.

Hilbert Basis Theorem 33. Let R be an integral domain which has the basis property (or equivalently the chain of divisors property). Then the ring of polynomials $R[x]$ also has this property.

Proof: Let S be an ideal in $R[x]$. We shall show that S has a finite basis. To do this consider the set N in R consisting of all coefficients of the highest powers of all polynomials in S and the zero element in R. That is, if $\phi(x) = \alpha_0 x^p + \alpha_1 x^{p-1} + \cdots \in S$, then $\alpha_0 \in N$. We assert that N is an ideal in R. For suppose a and b are elements in N. Then there exist polynomials $f(x)$ and $g(x)$ in S such that

$$f(x) = ax^n + a'x^{n-1} + \cdots$$

and

$$g(x) = bx^m + b'x^{m-1} + \cdots$$

We may assume without loss of generality that $n \geq m$. Since S is an ideal,

$$f(x) + x^{n-m}g(x) = (ax^n + a'x^{n-1} + \cdots) + (bx^n + b'x^{n-1} + \cdots)$$
$$= (a + b)x^n + (a' + b')x^{n-1} + \cdots$$

is in S, and hence by definition, $a + b$ is in N. Similarly if $c \in R$,

$$cf(x) = cax^n + ca'x^{n-1} + \cdots$$

is in S and hence $ca = ac$ is in N. We easily conclude that N is an ideal.

By hypothesis, N has a finite basis. Say $N = (\alpha_1, \alpha_2, \cdots, \alpha_r)$. Hence there exist polynomials $f_i(x)$ in S such that

$$f_i(x) = \alpha_i x^{n_i} + \alpha_i' x^{n_i-1} + \cdots$$

We shall use the polynomials $f_i(x)$ to construct a basis for the ideal S. Let S_1 be the ideal generated by $f_1(x), f_2(x), \cdots, f_r(x)$,

$$S_1 = (f_1(x), f_2(x), \cdots, f_r(x))$$

and let n be the maximum of the finite number of integers, n_i, $i = 1, 2,$ $\cdots, r$. Suppose that $\psi(x) = \alpha x^p + \alpha' x^{p-1} + \cdots$ is any polynomial in S of degree $p \geq n$. Then by the definition of N, $\alpha \in N$. Hence

$$\alpha = \sum_{i=1}^{r} \lambda_i \alpha_i,$$

where the λ_i are in R. (Since R is commutative with unity element, it is unnecessary to include terms of the form $\alpha_i \lambda_i'$ and numerical multiples of the α_i.) Consider the polynomial $\phi(x)$:

$$\phi(x) = \psi(x) - \sum_{i=1}^{r} (\lambda_i x^{p-n_i}) f_i(x).$$

The coefficient of x^p in this polynomial is $\alpha - \sum \lambda_i \alpha_i = 0$ and hence ϕ is of degree less than p. We may therefore write $\psi(x) \equiv \phi(x)$ (S_1), where $\phi(x)$ is a polynomial of degree less than p. Proceeding in this fashion we can construct a polynomial $\chi(x)$ such that $\psi(x) \equiv \chi(x)$ (S_1) and the degree of $\chi(x)$ is less than n.

It remains but to show that by adding only a finite number of elements, $h_1(x), h_2(x), \cdots, h_q(x)$ in S to S_1 we can construct an ideal such that every polynomial $\omega(x)$ (in S) of degree less than n is congruent to zero modulo $(S_1, h_1, h_2, \cdots, h_q)$, that is,

$$\omega(x) \equiv 0 \quad (S_1, h_1, \cdots, h_q).$$

But if this be the case it implies $S \subseteq (S_1, h_1, \cdots, h_q)$. Clearly $(S_1, h_1, \cdots, h_q) \subseteq S$, since $f_1, \cdots, f_r, h_1, \cdots, h_q$ are all in S. Hence $S = (S_1, h_1(x), \cdots, h_q(x))$ and our theorem will be proved.

Consider the totality of all coefficients of the x^{n-1} terms in all polynomials of degree $n - 1$ in S. As above, we can easily show that together with the zero element, this set forms an ideal N_1 in R. By hypothesis, N_1 has a finite basis, say $N_1 = (\beta_1, \cdots, \beta_s)$. Hence there exist polynomials $g_j(x)$ in S such that

$$g_j(x) = \beta_j x^{n-1} + \beta_j' x^{n-2} + \cdots.$$

Let S_2 be the ideal generated by $g_1(x), g_2(x), \cdots, g_s(x)$:

$$S_2 = (g_1(x), g_2(x), \cdots, g_s(x)).$$

Then, as above, we can show that every polynomial $\omega(x)$ in S is congruent modulo (S_1, S_2) to a polynomial $\zeta(x)$ of degree less than $n - 1$:

$$\omega(x) \equiv \zeta(x) \quad (S_1, S_2).$$

In at most n steps we can construct an ideal $(S_1, S_2, \cdots, S_t)$, $t \leq n$, such that $\omega(x) \equiv \delta \quad (S_1, S_2, \cdots, S_t)$ and $\delta \in R$. The set of all δ forms an ideal N_{t+1} in R and by hypothesis it has a finite basis. Hence

$$\omega(x) \equiv 0 \quad (S_1, S_2, \cdots, S_t, N_{t+1}).$$

Since every ideal S_i contains at most a finite number of elements of S, we see that $(S_1, \cdots, S_t, N_{t+1})$ contains only a finite number of elements of S, and by our previous remarks,

$$S = (S_1, S_2, \cdots, S_t, N_{t+1}).$$

EXERCISES

2.1. Let k be an integer. Let R be the set of all integers

$$R: \quad \{0, \pm k, \pm 2k, \pm 3k, \cdots\}$$

in which ordinary addition and multiplication have been defined. Prove that R is a commutative ring. What can you say if $k = 1$, if $k = 0$?

2.2. Let V be the group introduced in Exercise 1.9 of Chapter 1. Define multiplication in V by the equation

$$\alpha\beta = \{\alpha_1\beta_1, \alpha_2\beta_2, \cdots, \alpha_n\beta_n\}.$$

Prove that V is a commutative ring with a unity element.

2.3. Let p be a prime number. Prove that the set of integers R,

$$R: \quad \{0, 1, 2, \cdots, p - 1\}$$

form a commutative ring with a unity element under addition modulo p and multiplication modulo p.

2.4. Show that the totality of real numbers forms a ring under the operations of addition and multiplication.

2.5. Show that the totality of complex numbers under the operations of ordinary addition and multiplication forms a ring.

2.6. Show that the rings of Exercises 2.3, 2.4, and 2.5 are also fields.

2.7. Prove that the rings of Exercises 2.1 and 2.2 are *not* sfields.

2.8. Let R be the set of all pairs of integers (a,b), $b \neq 0$ where $(a,b) = (c,d)$ if and only if $a = c$ and $b = d$. Define addition and multiplication of elements in R by the equations

$$(a,b) + (c,d) = (ad + bc, bd)$$
$$(a,b)(c,d) = (ac, bd).$$

Prove that R is not a ring.

2.9. Let R be the set of all pairs of real numbers (a,b) where $(a,b) = (c,d)$ if and only if $a = c$ and $b = d$. Define addition and multiplication by the equations

$$(a,b) + (c,d) = (a + c, b + d)$$
$$(a,b)(c,d) = (ac - bd, bc + ad).$$

Prove that R is a field.

2.10. Let C be the class of all functions $f(x)$ of the real variable x defined and continuous on the unit interval $[0,1]$. Show that C is a commutative ring with unity element under ordinary addition and multiplication.

2.11. A *Gaussian integer* g is a complex number,

$$g = a + ib,$$

where a and b are integers. Show that the totality of Gaussian integers forms a ring with respect to ordinary addition and multiplication of complex numbers.

2.12. Let $R[x]$ be the set of all polynomials

$$a_0 x^n + a_1 x^{n-1} + \cdots + a_n$$

in a single variable x where the coefficients a_i are integers. Prove that $R[x]$ is a commutative ring with a unity element.

2.13. Let R be a ring which has the property that $a^2 = a$ for every element a in R. Prove that R is a commutative ring.

2.14. In the ring V of Exercise 2.2, show that there exist *divisors of zero*. That is, show the existence of elements α and β in V, both unequal to zero, which have the property that their product is zero, viz.:

$$\alpha\beta = 0,$$

where 0 is the identity element of the additive group.

2.15. Prove that the real numbers form a subring of the complex numbers under ordinary addition and multiplication.

2.16. Prove that the ring of integers Z is a subring of the Gaussian integers G under ordinary addition and multiplication.

2.17. Let R and S be two distinct rings. Let $R \times S$ be the set of all pairs (a,α) where a is in R and α is in S. Prove that $R \times S$ is a ring if addition is defined by the equation

$$(a,\alpha) + (b,\beta) = (a + b, \alpha + \beta)$$

and multiplication by the equation

$$(a,\alpha)(b,\beta) = (ab, \alpha\beta),$$

where a, b are in R and α, β are in S. Also prove that the mappings

$$\phi: \quad (a, \alpha) \to (a, 0)$$

and

$$\psi: \quad (a, \alpha) \to (0, \alpha)$$

are homomorphisms.

2.18. Let R be the ring introduced in Exercise 2.1. Define a multiplication $*$ in R such that with respect to ordinary addition and $*$, R becomes a ring isomorphic to the ring of integers Z.

2.19. Let R be an algebraic system which, except for commutativity of addition, is a ring. If there exists a left cancellation law; that is, $ab = ac$ with $a \neq 0$ implies $b = c$; prove that R is a ring.

2.20. Imbed the ring $\mathfrak{L}$ of absolutely integrable functions in a ring R with a unity element. What is the unity element in R?

2.21. Imbed the ring of even integers in a ring R with a unity element. How does R compare with Z?

2.22. Which of the rings of Exercises 2.1, 2.2, 2.3, 2.10, 2.11, 2.12 are integral domains?

2.23. Show that any ring with a finite number of elements which is free of divisors of zero and has a unity is a sfield.

2.24. Is the symbol $\leq$ (less than or equal to) an equivalence relation when applied to real numbers?

2.25. Let S be the set of all lines in a plane. Are the geometric notions of perpendicularity, $\perp$, and parallelism, $\parallel$, equivalence relations?

2.26. Let C be the class of all real valued functions $f(x)$ of the real variable x which are defined and bounded on the unit interval $[0,1]$. We shall write $f(x) \sim g(x)$ if $f(x)$ and $g(x)$ differ at only a finite number of points. Is $\sim$ an equivalence relation?

2.27. Let Z be the totality of integers $0, \pm 1, \pm 2, \cdots$. Let p be a prime number. We shall say two integers r and s are *equivalent*, written $r \sim s$, if p divides $r - s$. Show that $\sim$ is an equivalence relation and decompose Z into equivalence classes.

2.28. Let G be a group and H a subgroup of G. Consider the decomposition of G according to cosets of H. Are cosets equivalence classes? How do you define an equivalence relation in this case?

2.29. Construct the field of quotients of the ring of even integers. How does this field compare with the field of rational numbers?

2.30. Construct the field of quotients of the ring of Gaussian integers.

2.31. Prove that if R and S are isomorphic commutative rings without divisors of zero, then their quotient fields are isomorphic.

2.32. Let R and R^* be the rings of Theorem 2. Show that the subring R of R^* is an ideal.

2.33. Do the integers form an ideal in the ring of rational numbers?

2.34. (Cf. Exercise 2.17). Find the set of elements N in $R \times S$ which map onto the zero element of R under the homomorphism ϕ and prove that N is an ideal.

2.35. Construct the residue class rings of the ideals of Exercises 2.32 and 2.34.

2.36. If R is a ring with a unity element and N is an ideal properly contained in R, prove that the ring of remainder classes R/N has a unity element.

2.37. If R is a ring and N_1 and N_2 are ideals in R, prove that the intersection of N_1 and N_2 is also an ideal.

2.38. Let R be a ring and (M) the ideal generated by an arbitrary set of elements M in R. Prove that (M) is the smallest ideal in R containing M.

2.39. Let Z be the ring of integers and p a prime number. Let (p) be the principal ideal generated by p. Prove that the ring of remainder classes $Z/(p)$ is a field.

2.40. Construct the principal ideals (3), (4), (5) in the ring of integers Z.

2.41. Is the ring of remainder classes $Z/(4)$ a field?

2.42. If p and q are distinct prime numbers in the ring of integers Z, construct the ideal (p,q) generated by p and q.

2.43. If $a_1, a_2, \cdots, a_n$ is any set of integers in the ring Z, prove that there exists an element a in Z such that the ideals generated by a and $a_1, a_2, \cdots, a_n$, respectively, are identical, that is, $(a) = (a_1, a_2, \cdots, a_n)$.

2.44. Which of the principal ideals of Exercise 2.40 are prime ideals?

2.45. Consider the principal ideals (2), (5) and $(1 + i)$ in the ring of Gaussian integers. Are these ideals prime?

2.46. If G is the ring of Gaussian integers, is the ring of remainder classes $G/(1 + i)$ a field?

2.47. Let Z be the ring of integers. Show that the ring of remainder classes $Z/(9)$ generated by the principal ideal (9) is not a domain of integrity.

2.48. We call an ideal N in a ring R a *radical ideal* if a^n in N implies a is in N. Prove that every prime ideal is a radical ideal.

2.49. We call an ideal N in a ring R a *primary ideal* if ab in N with a not in N implies b^n is in N for some integer n. Prove that every prime ideal is a primary ideal.

2.50. A nonzero element a in a ring R is called a *nilpotent* element if there exists a positive integer n such that $a^n = 0$. Prove that if N is a radical ideal in R, then R/N has no nilpotent elements.

2.51. Let N be a primary ideal in a ring R. Prove that every divisor of zero in R/N is nilpotent.

2.52. Prove that the intersection of every set of prime ideals is radical.

2.53. Let R be a commutative ring and x an indeterminate. Consider the subset S of $R[x]$ consisting of all elements of the form $a_0 x^0 + 0x + 0x^2 + \cdots$. Prove that S is isomorphic to R.

2.54. Let R be an integral domain and let $R[x]$ be the ring of polynomials over R. Prove that $R[x]$ is an integral domain.

2.55. Let R be a commutative ring and let x be an indeterminate. Consider the set $R[[x]]$ of all formal power series, that is, the set of all terms of the form $a_0 x^0 + a_1 x + a_2 x^2 + \cdots$, $a_i \in R$, where an infinite number of the a_i may be distinct from zero. If addition and multiplication of power series are defined in the expected fashion, prove that $R[[x]]$ is a commutative ring.

2.56. Let R be a commutative ring. Let $x_1, x_2, \cdots, x_n$ be indeterminates. Prove that $R[x_1, x_2, \cdots, x_n]$ is a commutative ring.

2.57. If R is a commutative ring without divisors of zero and $x_1, x_2, \cdots, x_n$ are indeterminates, prove that $R[x_1, x_2, \cdots, x_n]$ is free of divisors of zero.

2.58. Let R be a commutative ring and $R[x]$ the ring of polynomials over R. Let α be a fixed element in R. Consider the set S of all elements $f(\alpha)$ where $f(x)$ is an element in $R[x]$, $f(x) = \sum a_j x^j$. Under the mapping

$$\phi: \quad f(x) \to f(\alpha)$$

prove that ϕ is a homomorphism of $R[x]$ onto S.

2.59. Let R be a commutative ring and let $R[x]$ be the ring of polynomials over R. Let α be a fixed element in R. Consider the set N of all polynomials $f(x)$ in $R[x]$ such that $f(\alpha) = 0$. Prove that N is an ideal.

2.60. In the previous problem let M be the set of all elements in R of the form $f(\alpha)$, where $f(x) \in R[x]$. Prove that M is a ring isomorphic to $R[x]/N$.

2.61. Prove that the ideal $(2,x)$ is a prime ideal in the ring of polynomials $Z[x]$. Is it a maximal ideal?

2.62. Prove that the ring of integers Z is a principal ideal ring.

2.63. Prove that the ring of Gaussian integers is a p.i.r.

2.64. Let R be a commutative ring. Prove that the ring of polynomials over R in two indeterminates x and y is not a p.i.r.

2.65. Is the principal ideal (xy) in the ring of polynomials $Z[x,y]$ a prime ideal? Is it a maximal ideal?

2.66. Consider the ideal (x,y) in $Z[x,y]$. Is (x,y) principal? Prime? Maximal?

2.67. Let R be a p.i.r. which is also an integral domain. Prove that every prime ideal in R distinct from the null ideal is maximal.

2.68. Prove that every field is a p.i.r.

2.69. Prove that the ring of integers is a Euclidean ring.

2.70. Prove that the ring of even integers is a p.i.r. but not a Euclidean ring.

2.71. Let Δ be a field. Is the ring of polynomials $\Delta[x_1, x_2, \cdots, x_n]$ a Euclidean ring?

2.72. If D is an integral domain and a and b are two nonzero elements in D, prove that $(ab) \subseteq (a)$. If neither a nor b is a unit, prove the stronger result that $(ab) \subset (a)$.

2.73. If D is an integral domain and ϵ is a unit in D, prove that the principal ideal generated by ϵ is the whole ring D.

2.74. Let R be a p.i.r. which is also an integral domain. Let p be a prime element in R which divides $a_1 a_2 \cdots a_n$, where $a_i \in R$. Prove that p divides some a_k, $k = 1, 2, \cdots, n$.

2.75. Let $\Delta[x]$ be the ring of polynomials over the rational field Δ. Define prime element in $\Delta[x]$ and prove that if $f(x)$ divides $\phi(x)\psi(x)$, where $f(x), \phi(x), \psi(x)$ are in $\Delta[x]$ and $f(x)$ is prime; then $f(x)$ divides $\phi(x)$ or $\psi(x)$.

2.76. Let D be an integral domain. Let U be the set of all units in D. Prove that U is a multiplicative subgroup of D.

2.77. Let Δ be the field of rational numbers and $\Delta[x]$ the ring of polynomials over Δ. Decompose the following elements of $\Delta[x]$ into prime factors:

$$f_1(x) = 2x^2 + 7x - 4$$
$$f_2(x) = 6x^2 - 21x - 12$$
$$f_3(x) = \tfrac{1}{2}x^2 + \tfrac{2}{3}x - 3$$
$$f_4(x) = x^3 - \tfrac{2}{3}x + \tfrac{4}{3}$$
$$f_5(x) = \tfrac{2}{3}x^3 - 2x^2 - 2x + 1$$
$$f_6(x) = x^5 - 2x^4 + 2x^2 - x$$
$$f_7(x) = x^n - 1, \quad n \text{ a positive integer.}$$

2.78. In the ring of integers Z, find by use of the Euclidean algorithm a G.C.D. of the following pairs of numbers.

$$a = 2321 \quad \text{and} \quad b = 7085$$
$$a = 172 \quad \text{and} \quad b = 1024$$
$$a = 9650 \quad \text{and} \quad b = 455.$$

Also determine the integers α and β such that $d = a\alpha + b\beta$, where d is the G.C.D. of a and b, in all cases.

2.79. Let Δ be the field of real numbers. By using the Euclidean algorithm find a G.C.D. of the following pairs of elements in $\Delta[x]$.

$$a(x) = x^3 + x + 1 \qquad \text{and} \quad b(x) = x^2 + 1$$
$$a(x) = x^4 + 4x^3 + 6x^2 + 4x + 1 \quad \text{and} \quad b(x) = x^3 + 3x^2 + 3x + 1$$
$$a(x) = x^5 - 7x^3 + 3x^2 - 2x + 1 \quad \text{and} \quad b(x) = x^2 - 1.$$

2.80. In Exercise 2.79 determine the polynomials $\phi(x)$ and $\psi(x)$ such that

$$d = \phi a + \psi b$$

where d is a G.C.D. of a and b, in all cases.

2.81. Let D be an integral domain in which the unique factorization theorem holds. Let $f(x) = a_0 x^m + a_1 x^{m-1} + \cdots + a_m$ and $g(x) = b_0 x^n + b_1 x^{n-1} + \cdots + b_n$ be two elements in $D[x]$. Prove that if $d \in D$ divides every coefficient of the polynomial $f(x)g(x)$, then it divides every product $a_i b_j$.

2.82. If the unique factorization theorem holds in an integral domain D, show that it holds in the polynomial domain $D[x_1, x_2, \cdots, x_n]$.

2.83. Let D be an integral domain in which the unique factorization theorem holds. Let Δ be the field of quotients of D. Prove that if a polynomial $f(x)$ is prime in $D[x]$, it is also prime in $\Delta[x]$.

2.84. Let Δ be the field of rational numbers. We know that $\Delta[x,y]$ is not a Euclidean ring. However, by letting $K = \Delta[x]$ and considering the ring of polynomials $K[y]$, see if you can devise an analog of the Euclidean algorithm for polynomials in two variables. (Hint: cf. Bôcher. *Introduction to Higher Algebra*, Macmillan, 1907, Chapter XVI.)

2.85. Let $f(x) \in \Delta[x]$ where Δ is a field, and let $\alpha_i \in \Delta$, $i = 1, 2, \cdots, n$ be n distinct zeros of $f(x)$. Prove that

$$f(x) = p(x)(x - \alpha_1)(x - \alpha_2) \cdots (x - \alpha_n)$$

where $p(x) \in \Delta[x]$.

2.86. Prove that if a is an arbitrary element in a commutative ring R, considered as a subring of $R[x]$, then the derivative a' of a is zero.

2.87. If $f(x)$ and $g(x)$ are elements in a commutative ring $R[x]$ and $f'(x)$ and $g'(x)$ are their derivatives, prove that

$$(f + g)' = f' + g' \quad \text{and} \quad (fg)' = f'g + fg'.$$

2.88. Prove that a polynomial of degree n over $\Delta[x]$ has at most n distinct zeros in the field Δ.

2.89. Prove that if a commutative ring R with unity element has the basis property, then so has the ring $R[[x]]$ of formal power series. (Cf. Exercise 2.55.)

CHAPTER 3

Fields

3.1 Prime Fields

The theory of fields represents a culmination of the study of groups and rings. A group was an algebraic system in which one binary operation was defined. This system was closed under this operation and every element had an inverse. We extended our system to rings in which a second binary operation was defined. The ring was also closed under this operation, but no inverses were postulated. These two operations were connected by the laws of distributivity. As the complexity of the structure of our algebraic systems increased, the theorems, while more difficult, had greater content. In the present chapter we shall systematically study the theory of fields and sfields.

We recall that a field was defined (Section 2.1) as a commutative ring in which the nonzero elements formed a multiplicative group. This, in effect, represents a generalization of what is generally called a "field" or "domain of rationality" in elementary algebra. The rational numbers, the real numbers, the complex numbers, are all examples of fields. They are the ones which are used in analysis. However, we shall investigate *abstract* fields, that is, systems, which, roughly speaking, are additive and multiplicative groups. We shall see that many theorems which are true for the special fields of analysis are also true for arbitrary fields. However, we shall also see that there are certain systems of double composition which satisfy the axioms of a field, yet are of a very different character from the "fields of analysis." These are the *finite fields* which we have briefly encountered in Section 2.15. In the present chapter we shall consider properties of abstract fields in general and then consider special fields, as for example, the finite fields and the field of algebraic numbers.

Our immediate task will be to classify fields with a view to establishing the possible structure of the field and then consider some very important results relating to field adjunctions (cf. Section 3.2).

Consider, then, an arbitrary skew field Σ. It may be that Σ contains a subset Ω which is also a sfield. If it does, we call Ω a *subfield* of Σ. The intersection of any set of subfields of a given sfield Σ is again a subfield of Σ. Let Π be the intersection of all subfields of Σ (except the null field consisting of the zero element alone). Then Π is called the *prime field* of Σ.

Clearly a prime field is a *sfield*. Also, it is unique, that is, a sfield Σ contains only one prime field. One could also define a prime field Π as a sfield which contains no proper subfields. We leave it to the reader to show that this definition is equivalent to the one we have given above.

In the present section we shall investigate the structure of an arbitrary prime field Π and arrive at the remarkable result that Π is either isomorphic to the field of rational numbers K or else is isomorphic to the ring of residue classes $Z/(p)$, where p is a prime number. Before starting the theorem we prove a lemma.

Lemma. Let Π be a prime field and let e be the unity element of Π. Then the integral multiples of e, that is, ne, where n is in Z, form a commutative ring P with unity element.

Proof: If n and m are integers (in Z), then clearly

$$ne + me = (n + m)e$$

and

$$(ne)(me) = nme$$

by definition of the symbols ne and me. Hence P is closed with respect to addition and multiplication. Also $0e = 0 \in P$ and $1 \cdot e = e \in P$. And if $ne \in P$, $- ne \in P$ and $ne + (- ne) = 0$ is in P. We see therefore that P is an additive abelian group, that it has a unity element e and is closed with respect to multiplication. The distributivity laws, for example,

$$qe(ne + me) = qe[(n + m)e] = [q(n + m)]e = (qn + qm)e$$
$$= qne + qme = (qe)(ne) + (qe)(me)$$

are evident, and hence P is a commutative ring with a unity element.

We now state and prove the crucial theorem of our discussion.

Theorem 1. Let Π be a prime field. Let Z be the ring of integers and K the field of rational numbers. Then Π is a field which is either isomorphic to K or isomorphic to the ring of remainder classes $Z/(p)$, where p is a prime number.

Proof: Let P be the ring of integral multiples of e defined in the lemma. We define a mapping ψ of Z onto P by

$$\psi: \quad m \to me.$$

By the definition of addition and multiplication of elements in P (cf. the lemma), we see that ψ is a homomorphism mapping Z onto P,

$$\psi: \quad Z \to P.$$

Now let N be that ideal in Z which maps onto the zero element of P under the above homomorphism. By Theorem 10 of Chapter 2, Z/N is isomorphic to P,

$$Z/N \approx P.$$

Since P is a subset of a sfield, Π, it has no divisors of zero. Hence Z/N can have no divisors of zero. Since Z/N is a commutative ring with a unity element, we conclude that Z/N is an integral domain. By Theorem 12 of Chapter 2 we see that N is a prime ideal, and from Theorem 26,

$$N = (p)$$

where p is a prime element in Z or zero. Three cases arise.

Case 1. p is a prime number and (p) is a nontrivial prime ideal [that is, (p) is unequal to the null ideal or the unit ideal].

Case 2 $p = 0$ and (p) is the null ideal.

Case 3. $p = 1$ and (p) is the unit ideal.

Case 1. Suppose p is a prime number. Then

$$Z/(p) \approx P.$$

We have seen in Section 2.15 that $Z/(p)$ is a field. Now $P \subseteq \Pi$ and we have shown that P is a field. Hence we must have $P = \Pi$, since a prime field contains no proper subfields. Therefore

$$Z/(p) \approx \Pi$$

and Π is a finite field.

Case 2. Suppose $p = 0$. Then the homomorphism ψ

$$\psi: \quad Z \to P$$

becomes an isomorphism,

$$Z \approx P$$

since $Z/(p) = Z/(0) = Z$.

Now P is not a field, since the ring of integers Z is not a field. Since $P \subseteq \Pi$, and Π is a field, Π must contain not only P but the multiplicative inverses of all nonzero elements in P. That is, Π must contain the quotient field Q of P, $Q \subseteq \Pi$. The field of quotients of Z is the rational field K. Since $Z \approx P$ we conclude that their quotient fields K and Q (respectively) are also isomorphic,

$$K \approx Q,$$

(cf. Exercise 2.31). Since Π has no proper subfields, we see that $Q = \Pi$ and hence

$$K \approx \Pi\,;$$

that is, the prime field Π is isomorphic to the field of rational numbers.

Case 3. Suppose $p = 1$. Then (p) is the unit ideal and the ring of remainder classes $Z/(1)$ contains only the zero element. Since

$$Z/(1) \approx P$$

this implies that P has at most one element. This is a contradiction, since in particular 0 and e are in P. Hence we must rule out the case $p = 1$.

If p is a prime number, then $Z/(p)$ is a *finite* field and the number p is called the *characteristic* of the prime field Π or the characteristic of the original sfield Σ. We say $Z/(p)$ is "a field of characteristic p." In any such field

$$pa = 0$$

for all $a \in Z/(p)$ since $p \in (p)$. An important property of the characteristic is that it is the smallest positive integer with the property that $pa = 0$ for all $a \in Z/(p)$. (Cf. Theorem 2 below.)

If the prime field has an infinite number of elements (Case 2) then we call Π (or Σ) a "field of characteristic zero." One reason for this terminology is that the equation

$$ne = 0$$

implies that $n = 0$. All the fields of classical analysis, namely the rationals, reals, and complex numbers are fields of characteristic zero since K is the prime field in each case.

Theorem 2. Let $Z/(p)$ be a finite field where p, a prime number, is the characteristic of $Z/(p)$. Then p is the smallest positive integer with the property that $pa = 0$ for all a in $Z/(p)$.

Proof: It is clear that pa *does* equal zero for all a in $Z/(p)$ since $pa \equiv 0$ (p). Suppose now that

$$na = 0$$

for all $a \in Z/(p)$, where n is an integer, $0 < n < p$. Since the integers Z form a Euclidean ring without divisors of zero (cf. Theorem 27 of Chapter 2),

$$d = rn + sp$$

where r and s are integers (in Z) and d is a G.C.D. of n and p. Multiplying this equation by a, we obtain

$$da = rna + spa.$$

By hypothesis, $pa = 0$, $na = 0$. Hence $da = 0$. Since p is prime and n is less than p, we must have d a unit, that is,

$$d = \pm 1.$$

Hence

$$1 \cdot a = 0 \qquad \text{or} \qquad -1 \cdot a = 0$$

for all $a \in Z/(p)$. This is absurd; hence p must be the smallest positive integer with the property that $pa = 0$ for all a in $Z/(p)$.

From the above theorem we can conclude that if Σ is a sfield and p is the characteristic of its prime field Π, then

$$pa = 0$$

for all a in Σ. Since Π is a field, the identity e of Σ is in Π. Now suppose

$$pa = b \neq 0.$$

Then a^{-1} exists in Σ, so that in Σ,

$$pe = paa^{-1} = ba^{-1} \neq 0.$$

But $e \in \Pi$; hence $pe = 0$ from the previous theorem, which is a contradiction.

If a sfield Σ has characteristic zero, then it must contain an infinite number of elements, since its prime field $\Pi \subseteq \Sigma$ already has an infinite number of elements. The converse is not true. That is, Σ may be a sfield with an infinite number of elements and yet its prime field may contain only a finite number of elements and hence be a field of characteristic p. For example, let $Z/(2)(x)$ represent all rational functions of the indeterminate x with coefficients in $Z/(2)$. For example,

$$\frac{a_0 + a_1x + \cdots + a_nx^n}{b_0 + b_1x + \cdots + b_mx^m}$$

is a typical element in $Z/(2)(x)$, where the a_i and b_j are in $Z/(2)$, that is, they are either zeros or ones. The reader may easily verify that $Z/(2)(x)$ is a field with an infinite number of elements, yet the prime field of $Z/(2)(x)$ is $Z/(2)$. Hence $Z/(2)(x)$ is a field of characteristic two.

Finally, if Σ contains only a finite number of elements, then it must be a field of characteristic p. This is true because the prime field Π of Σ is contained in Σ and hence can have only a finite number of elements. By Theorem 1, there exists a prime number p such that $\Pi \approx Z/(p)$.

As a concrete illustration, let us consider an example of a finite field and determine its characteristic. We recall that the ideal $(1 + i)$ is prime in the ring of Gaussian integers, G. Since G is a Euclidean ring without divisors of zero, every prime ideal is maximal, and by Theorem 13 of Chapter 2 the ring of residue classes $G/(1 + i)$ is a field. The elements of $G/(1 + i)$ are the remainder classes

$$0 + (1 + i) \qquad \text{and} \qquad 1 + (1 + i).$$

It is clear that $G/(1 + i)$ is isomorphic to $Z/(2)$ and hence $G/(1 + i)$ is a field of characteristic two.

Another less trivial example is $G/(3)$. We shall show that in this case the prime field is *properly* contained in $G/(3)$. First we must show that (3) is a *prime* ideal. Once we have done this we shall be able to conclude by the same argument used in the previous paragraph that $G/(3)$ is a field. It is not immediately obvious that (3) *is* prime in G even though 3 is a prime number *in* Z. For example, 2 is a prime number in Z, yet 2 is *not* a prime element in G since $2 = (1 + i)(1 - i)$. However, we shall show that 3 has no factors except units in G. Suppose

$$3 = (\alpha + i\beta)(\gamma + i\delta)$$

where $\alpha, \beta, \gamma, \delta$ are integers. It is clear that

$$g(3) = g(\alpha + i\beta)g(\gamma + i\delta)$$

or

$$9 = (\alpha^2 + \beta^2)(\gamma^2 + \delta^2),$$

where g is the Euclidean g function of Theorem 21, Chapter 2. Now if $\alpha^2 + \beta^2 = 1$, then $\alpha + i\beta$ would have to be a unit. Hence we must have

$$\alpha^2 + \beta^2 = 3 \qquad \text{and} \qquad \gamma^2 + \delta^2 = 3.$$

But there exist no integers $\alpha, \beta, \gamma, \delta$ which satisfy the above equations. We conclude, therefore, that (3) is a prime ideal in the ring of Gaussian integers G.

The elements of the field $G/(3)$ are residue classes. If $\alpha + i\beta$ is an arbitrary element of G, then it must be congruent modulo (3) to one of the elements of $G/(3)$. Since the division algorithm holds in G, we may write,every $\alpha + i\beta$ in G in the form

$$\alpha + i\beta = 3(a + ib) + (\zeta + i\omega)$$

where $\zeta = 0, 1$ or 2 and $\omega = 0, 1$ or 2. That is,

$$\alpha + i\beta \equiv \zeta + i\omega \quad (3).$$

Hence the elements of $G/(3)$ are

$$0 + 0i + (3)$$
$$1 + 0i + (3)$$
$$2 + 0i + (3)$$
$$0 + i + (3)$$
$$1 + i + (3)$$
$$2 + i + (3)$$
$$0 + 2i + (3)$$
$$1 + 2i + (3)$$
$$2 + 2i + (3).$$

In the notation introduced in the last chapter we could write

$$\overline{0 + 0i}, \quad \overline{1 + 0i}, \quad \text{etc.}$$

in place of

$$0 + 0i + (3), \quad 1 + 0i + (3), \quad \text{etc.}$$

where

$$0 + 0i + (3) \rightarrow \overline{0 + 0i}$$
$$1 + 0i + (3) \rightarrow \overline{1 + 0i}$$
$$\cdot \quad \cdot \quad \cdot \quad \cdot \quad \cdot$$

under the natural homomorphism $\nu : G \rightarrow G/(3)$. However, for simplicity, it is convenient to drop the "bars" and call

$$0 + 0i$$
$$1 + 0i$$
$$\cdot \quad \cdot \quad \cdot \qquad \qquad (3.1)$$
$$2 + 2i$$

the elements of $G/(3)$, where it is understood that any two elements λ and μ in G are to be regarded as identical in $G/(3)$ if $\lambda \equiv \mu$ (3). Clearly none of the elements of Equation 3.1 is congruent to any other modulo (3). Hence $G/(3)$ is a field with nine elements. The reader may verify directly that $G/(3)$ *is* a field by constructing the "addition" and multi-plication table for $G/(3)$. For example, the multiplicative inverses of the nonzero elements of Equation 3.1 are:

$$1^{-1} = 1$$
$$2^{-1} = 2$$
$$i^{-1} = 2i$$
$$(1 + i)^{-1} = 2 + i$$
$$(2 + i)^{-1} = 1 + i$$
$$(2i)^{-1} = i$$
$$(1 + 2i)^{-1} = 2 + 2i$$
$$(2 + 2i)^{-1} = 1 + 2i.$$

The prime field Π of $G/(3)$ is $Z/(3)$, that is, it consists of the three elements

$$Z/(3): \qquad \{0, 1, 2\}$$

where addition and multiplication are to be interpreted as addition and multiplication modulo three. We see that $Z/(3)$ is properly contained in $G/(3)$, $Z/(3) \subset G/(3)$, and by the very definition of characteristic, $G/(3)$ is a field of characteristic three. Note that the number of ele-ments in $G/(3)$ is nine, that is, it is a power of the characteristic. This is a general property of finite fields which will be proved in Section 3.5.

Fields of characteristic p have some unusual properties. For example, in a field Δ of characteristic two,

$$(a + b)^2 = a^2 + b^2$$

where $a \in \Delta$, $b \in \Delta$. This is easily shown, since

$$(a + b)^2 = a^2 + 2ab + b^2$$

and

$$2ab \equiv 0 \quad (2)$$

for all a and b. In general,

$$(a + b)^p = a^p + b^p$$

where a and b are elements in a field of characteristic p.

3.2 Field Adjunctions

When we studied the properties of abstract rings in the previous chapter we considered the important topic of *ring adjunction*. That is, if R were a commutative ring we considered the ring of polynomials $R[x]$ over R obtained by adjoining the indeterminate x to R. This concept led to many interesting theorems which extended and unified various special results of elementary algebra. An analogous process known as *field adjunction* exists for fields, and most of our future results in field theory will rest heavily on this concept.

Preliminary to proving the fundamental theorem (Theorem 3) concerning field adjunctions, let us consider a few special cases. If Δ is a field which is contained in a superfield Ξ, that is $\Delta \subseteq \Xi$, then we can consider an arbitrary element θ in Ξ. With this element θ, form all rational expressions of the form

$$\frac{a_0\theta^n + a_1\theta^{n-1} + \cdots + a_n}{b_0\theta^m + b_1\theta^{m-1} + \cdots + b_m} \tag{3.2}$$

where the a_i and b_j are elements in Δ and $b_0\theta^m + b_1\theta^{m-1} + \cdots + b_m$ is unequal to the zero element of Ξ. The totality of elements of the form of Equation 3.2 form a *field*. (The trivial proof of this fact will be left as an exercise for the reader.) This field is denoted by $\Delta(\theta)$; we say θ is *adjoined* to Δ and call the process *field adjunction*. (Cf. the discussion of the generation of a principal ideal in Section 2.8 of Chapter 2.) We shall consistently use parentheses ( ) for *field* adjunction, while brackets [ ] will be reserved for *ring* adjunction. In Ξ we could also consider the ring $\Delta[\theta]$ of all polynomials in θ whose coefficients lie in Δ. Clearly $\Delta[\theta]$ is contained in $\Delta(\theta)$.

The field $\Delta(\theta)$ is called an *extension field* of Δ and, in particular, a *simple field extension*, since we have adjoined only one element of Ξ. The process of adjoining a single element to Δ, for the same reason, is frequently spoken of as a *simple field adjunction*. Later we shall define and consider arbitrary field extensions.

We saw above that $\Delta[\theta]$ was contained in $\Delta(\theta)$. In certain cases $\Delta[\theta]$ may be identical with $\Delta(\theta)$, and in others $\Delta[\theta]$ may be properly contained in $\Delta(\theta)$. These two possibilities will be illustrated by concrete examples since they are typical of the situations that arise in the general case (cf. Theorem 3). Let, then, K be the field of rational numbers. Then K is a subfield of the complex numbers C. Since $i = \sqrt{-1}$ is an element of C, we may consider the simple field extension $K(i)$. This field contains all rational functions of the form

$$f(i) = \frac{a_0i^n + a_1i^{n-1} + \cdots + a_n}{b_0i^m + b_1i^{m-1} + \cdots + b_m}$$

where the a_i and b_j are rational numbers. But every power of i is either $\pm i$ or ± 1. Hence $f(i)$ may be written in the form

$$f(i) = \frac{\alpha_0i + \alpha_1}{\beta_0i + \beta_1}.$$

But, on multiplying numerator and denominator by $-\beta_0 i + \beta_1 \in K(i)$, we obtain

$$f(i) = \frac{(\alpha_0 i + \alpha_1)(-\beta_0 i + \beta_1)}{\beta_0^2 + \beta_1^2}$$

which is again of the form

$$f(i) = \alpha i + \beta$$

where α and β are rational numbers (elements of K). (Since by definition of a field extension, $b_0 i^m + b_1 i^{m-1} + \cdots + b_m$ is not the zero element of C, $\beta_0^2 + \beta_1^2 \neq 0$.) So we see that $f(i)$ is actually a *polynomial* in i, that is,

$$f(i) \in K[i].$$

Since $K[i] \subseteq K(i)$ and we have just shown $K(i) \subseteq K[i]$, it follows that

$$K(i) = K[i],$$

that is, the simple field extension $K(i)$ is identical with the ring of polynomials $K[i]$.

On the other hand, consider the field of real numbers E. The field of rational numbers K is properly contained in E. Now the number π is an element of E. Hence we may consider the simple field extension $K(\pi)$. The elements of $K(\pi)$ are rational expressions of the form

$$f(\pi) = \frac{a_0 \pi^n + a_1 \pi^{n-1} + \cdots + a_n}{b_0 \pi^m + b_1 \pi^{m-1} + \cdots + b_m}$$

where $a_i, b_j \in K$. In this case we assert $K[\pi] \subset K(\pi)$. For example, suppose $1/\pi$ were a polynomial in π, say

$$\frac{1}{\pi} = c_0 \pi^p + c_1 \pi^{p-1} + \cdots + c_p, \qquad c_0 \neq 0.$$

This would imply

$$c_0 \pi^{p+1} + c_1 \pi^p + \cdots + c_p \pi - 1 = 0.$$

But from our knowledge of analysis, we know that π satisfies no algebraic equation with rational coefficients. Hence the above expression is impossible and

$$K[\pi] \subset K(\pi).$$

In the first case, we call $K(i)$ an *algebraic extension* of K, and in the second, we call $K(\pi)$ a *transcendental extension* of K. It will be seen in Theorem 3 that these are the only two possible types of simple field extensions over an arbitrary field Δ.

We now proceed to the general case of field adjunctions over arbitrary fields.

Definition. Let Δ be an arbitrary field which is contained in some superfield Ξ, that is, $\Delta \subseteq \Xi$. Let M be a subset of the elements of Ξ. Then by the symbol $\Delta(M)$ we mean the intersection of all subfields of Ξ containing both Δ and M. We say that $\Delta(M)$ arises from Δ by the *adjunction* of the set M.

We leave it to the reader to prove that $\Delta(M)$ *is* a field and that every element of $\Delta(M)$ can be expressed as a rational function in the elements of M with elements of Δ as coefficients. By definition of a rational function, only a finite number of monomials appear. Hence every element of $\Delta(M)$ lies in a field $\Delta(T)$, where T is a *finite* subset of M. Of course we may have to use a different T for each element of $\Delta(M)$. Suppose that the elements of some T are $\{\alpha_1, \alpha_2, \cdots, \alpha_n\}$. Then we may write

$$\Delta(T) = \Delta(\alpha_1, \alpha_2, \cdots, \alpha_n).$$

We leave it to the reader to show that

$$\Delta(\alpha_1, \alpha_2, \cdots, \alpha_n)$$

and

$$\Delta(\alpha_1)(\alpha_2) \cdots (\alpha_n)$$

are the same fields. Hence we see that any finite field adjunction is equivalent to a sequence of simple field adjunctions. For $\Delta(\alpha_1)$ is a simple field extension of Δ, and if we let $\Omega = \Delta(\alpha_1)$, then $\Omega(\alpha_2)$ is a simple field extension of Ω.

In view of the above discussion, it seems natural that our first task should be to examine *simple* field extensions. The main structure theorem for simple field adjunctions is Theorem 3. Note the close analogy between its proof and the proof of Theorem 1.

Theorem 3. Let Δ be a field, Ξ a superfield containing Δ, and θ an arbitrary element in Ξ. Let x be an indeterminate and $\Delta[x]$ the ring of polynomials over Δ. Then $\Delta(\theta)$ is a field which is either isomorphic to $\Delta(x)$ or isomorphic to the ring of remainder classes $\Delta[x]/(\phi(x))$, where $\phi(x)$ is a prime element in $\Delta[x]$.

Proof: Since Δ and θ are in Ξ, we may consider the field $\Delta(\theta)$ obtained by the adjunction of the element θ to Δ and $\Delta(\theta) \subseteq \Xi$. This field must contain the ring of polynomials $\Delta[\theta]$, that is, the ring consisting of all elements of the form $\sum a_k \theta^k$, where the a_k are in Δ. If we consider the mapping ψ,

$$\psi: \qquad \sum a_k x^k \to \sum a_k \theta^k$$

of $\varDelta[x]$ onto $\varDelta[\theta]$, where $f(x) = \sum a_k x^k \in \varDelta[x]$ and $f(\theta) = \sum a_k \theta^k \in \varDelta[\theta]$ we easily see that it is a homomorphism,

$$\psi: \qquad \varDelta[x] \to \varDelta[\theta]$$

by the very definition of addition and multiplication of polynomials. By Theorem 10 of Chapter 2,

$$\varDelta[x]/N \approx \varDelta[\theta]$$

where N is that ideal in $\varDelta[x]$ which maps onto the zero element of $\varDelta[\theta]$ under the above homomorphism. Since $\varDelta[\theta]$ is a subset of a field, $\varDelta(\theta)$, it has no divisors of zero. Hence $\varDelta[x]/N$ is an integral domain. By Theorem 12 of Chapter 2, N is a prime ideal. As in the case of prime fields (cf. Theorem 1), three possibilities arise.

Case 1. $\quad$ N is a nontrivial prime ideal (that is, N is unequal to the null ideal or the unit ideal).

Case 2. $\quad$ N is the null ideal.

Case 3. $\quad$ N is the unit ideal.

Case 1. Suppose N is a nontrivial prime ideal. Since $\varDelta[x]$ is a principal ideal ring (cf. Theorem 16 of Chapter 2), $N = (\phi(x))$, where $\phi(x)$ is an element of $\varDelta[x]$. Since, further, N is prime, we know by the corollary to Theorem 26 of Chapter 2 that $\phi(x)$ is a prime element in $\varDelta[x]$; that is, its only factors are units and associated elements. From Exercise 2.67 and Theorem 13 of Chapter 2, we conclude that $\varDelta[x]/(\phi(x))$ is a field. But

$$\varDelta[x]/(\phi(x)) \approx \varDelta[\theta]$$

and $\varDelta[\theta] \subseteq \varDelta(\theta)$. Since $\varDelta[\theta]$ is already a field, we have $\varDelta[\theta] = \varDelta(\theta)$ and hence

$$\varDelta[x]/(\phi(x)) \approx \varDelta(\theta).$$

Case 2. Suppose N is the null ideal. Then the homomorphism

$$\psi: \qquad \varDelta[x] \to \varDelta[\theta]$$

becomes an isomorphism

$$\varDelta[x] \approx \varDelta[\theta]$$

since

$$\varDelta[x]/N = \varDelta[x]/(0) = \varDelta[x].$$

Now $\varDelta[\theta]$ is not a field, since the ring of polynomials $\varDelta[x]$ is not a field. However, from Exercise 2.31 of Chapter 2, the quotient fields of $\varDelta[x]$ and $\varDelta[\theta]$ are isomorphic, that is,

$$\varDelta(x) \approx \varDelta(\theta).$$

Hence $\varDelta(\theta)$ is isomorphic to the field of rational functions in an indeterminate x.

Case 3. If N is the unit ideal, then $\varDelta[x]/N = 0$, and since $\varDelta[\theta]$ is isomorphic to $\varDelta[x]/N$, $\varDelta[\theta]$ can have only one element. This is a contradiction.

In Case 1, that is, where $N = (\phi(x))$ is a nontrivial prime ideal, we say that the element θ is *algebraic* over $\varDelta$ and that $\varDelta(\theta)$ is a "simple algebraic extension of $\varDelta$." If $f(x)$ is any polynomial in the ideal N, then under the homomorphism $\psi\colon \varDelta[x] \to \varDelta[\theta]$, $f(x)$ is mapped onto $f(\theta)$. But by the fundamental isomorphism theorem (Theorem 10 of Chapter 2), the ideal N is mapped onto the zero element 0 of $\varDelta[\theta]$. Hence $f(\theta) = 0$. In other words, θ is a zero of $f(x)$. Now $\phi(x) \in N$ and hence $\phi(\theta) = 0$. We assert that $\phi(x)$ is the polynomial of minimal degree with the property that $\phi(\theta) = 0$. For suppose $g(x)$ were a polynomial of degree less than $\phi(x)$ with the property that $g(\theta) = 0$. Since θ is a zero of $g(x)$, this polynomial must be in N, since by definition, all preimages of the zero of $\varDelta[\theta]$ lie in N. But $\varDelta[x]$ is a p.i.r.; thus

$$g(x) = r(x)\phi(x), \qquad r(x) \in \varDelta[x].$$

But this is absurd, since the degree of ϕ exceeds that of g. The polynomial $\phi(x)$ is called the defining polynomial for the simple algebraic field extension $\varDelta(\theta)$, and $\phi(x) = 0$ is called the *defining equation*.

In Case 2 where N is the null ideal, we say θ is *transcendental* over $\varDelta$ and $\varDelta(\theta)$ is called "a simple transcendental extension of $\varDelta$." The field $K(\pi)$ considered before the proof of Theorem 3 is a transcendental extension of the field of rational numbers K, and $K(\pi)$ is isomorphic to $K(x)$. On the other hand, $K(i)$, the quotient field of the Gaussian integers, is an algebraic extension of K, and

$$K(i) \approx K[x]/(\phi(x))$$

where $\phi(x) = x^2 + 1$ is the defining polynomial for $K(i)$.

As an example, let us consider the problem of adjoining $\sqrt{2}$ to the rational field K where K and $\sqrt{2}$ can both be considered as belonging to the superfield E of real numbers. From our knowledge of analysis, we know that $\sqrt{2}$ is algebraic over the rational numbers. Furthermore, its defining equation is $\phi(x) = x^2 - 2 = 0$, since $\phi(x) = x^2 - 2 \in K[x]$ and $\phi(\sqrt{2}) = 0$ (in E). We also see that $\phi(x)$ is prime in $K[x]$ and hence

$$K(\sqrt{2}) \approx K[x]/(x^2 - 2).$$

By Theorem 3 we know that

$$K[\sqrt{2}] = K(\sqrt{2}).$$

That is, every rational function in powers of $\sqrt{2}$ with rational numbers as coefficients can be written as a polynomial in $\sqrt{2}$ with rational numbers as coefficients. By operating with congruences in the ring of remainder classes $K[x]/(x^2 - 2)$, let us determine, for example, the polynomial which equals the rational function

$$\frac{1}{x^4 - 7x^3 + 6x^2 + 9x + 4}.$$

Now

$x^4 - 7x^3 + 6x^2 + 9x + 4$
$$= x^2(x^2 - 2) - 7x(x^2 - 2) + 8(x^2 - 2) - 5x + 20$$
$$= (x^2 - 7x + 8)(x^2 - 2) - 5x + 20$$

and

$$(x^2 - 7x + 8)(x^2 - 2) - 5x + 20 \equiv -5x + 20 \quad \mathrm{mod}\ (x^2 - 2)$$

since

$$x^2 - 7x + 8 \in K[x].$$

Also

$$\frac{1}{-5x + 20} = \frac{-5x - 20}{25x^2 - 400} \equiv \frac{-5x - 20}{-350} \quad \mathrm{mod}\ (x^2 - 2).$$

Hence

$$\frac{1}{x^4 - 7x^3 + 6x^2 + 9x + 4} = \frac{x}{70} + \frac{2}{35}$$

in the field $K[x]/(x^2 - 2)$. On the other hand,

$$\frac{1}{(\sqrt{2})^4 - 7(\sqrt{2})^3 + 6(\sqrt{2})^2 + 9(\sqrt{2}) + 4} \in K(\sqrt{2})$$

and we see that

$$\frac{1}{(\sqrt{2})^4 - 7(\sqrt{2})^3 + 6(\sqrt{2})^2 + 9(\sqrt{2}) + 4}$$
$$= \frac{1}{4 - 14\sqrt{2} + 12 + 9\sqrt{2} + 4} = \frac{1}{20 - 5\sqrt{2}}$$
$$= \frac{1}{20 - 5\sqrt{2}} \cdot \frac{4 + \sqrt{2}}{4 + \sqrt{2}} = \frac{4 + \sqrt{2}}{70} = \frac{\sqrt{2}}{70} + \frac{2}{35}.$$

With the above example in mind we can consider a certain generalization of the "conjugate" of a number. We know from elementary algebra that the reciprocal of a complex number

$$\frac{1}{\alpha + i\beta}$$

can always be written as a complex number $\gamma + i\delta$ if we simply multiply numerator and denominator by the conjugate of $\alpha + i\beta$, that is, multiply by $\alpha - i\beta$,

$$\frac{1}{\alpha + i\beta} \cdot \frac{\alpha - i\beta}{\alpha - i\beta} = \frac{\alpha}{\alpha^2 + \beta^2} - i\frac{\beta}{\alpha^2 + \beta^2}.$$

Consider now the relatively complicated expression

$$\lambda = \frac{1}{3\sqrt[3]{25} - 4\sqrt[3]{5} + 7}.$$

We ask whether we can find a "conjugate" of $3\sqrt[3]{25} - 4\sqrt[3]{5} + 7$ such that if we multiply numerator and denominator by this "conjugate", λ will become a *polynomial* in $\sqrt[3]{5}$. The existence of such a "conjugate" is guaranteed by the above structure theorem. For, worded abstractly, let K be the field of rational numbers; then

$$K(\sqrt[3]{5}) \approx K[x]/(\phi(x)),$$

where $\phi(x) = x^3 - 5$ is the defining polynomial for $K(\sqrt[3]{5})$. Since $(\phi(x))$ is a nontrivial prime ideal, every element in $K(\sqrt[3]{5})$, for example, λ, is also an element in the ring of polynomials $K[\sqrt[3]{5}]$ since $K[\sqrt[3]{5}] = K(\sqrt[3]{5})$. Hence such a conjugate must exist.

Perhaps the easiest way to find such "conjugates" is by the use of the Euclidean algorithm. Let θ be an algebraic element over the rational field K. Let $f(x)$ be an element in $K[x]$ which is not in the ideal $(\phi(x))$ generated by the defining polynomial $\phi(x)$. (That is, $f(x)$ is *not* mapped onto the zero of $K[\theta]$ under the homomorphism $\psi : K[x] \to K[\theta]$.) Now

$$\frac{1}{f(\theta)} \in K(\theta).$$

We wish to find an $\alpha(\theta) \in K[\theta]$ such that

$$\frac{1}{f(\theta)} = \alpha(\theta).$$

Since $f(x) \notin (\phi(x))$ and $\phi(x)$ is prime, $f(x)$ and $\phi(x)$ have no common factors except units. Hence, since $K[x]$ is a Euclidean ring without divisors of zero (cf. Theorems 20 and 27 of Chapter 2) we know there exist polynomials $\alpha(x)$ and $\beta(x)$ in $K[x]$ such that

$$f(x)\alpha(x) + \phi(x)\beta(x) = 1.$$

In the ring of remainder classes $K[\theta] \approx K[x]/(\phi(x))$ and the above equation becomes

$$f(\theta)\alpha(\theta) + \phi(\theta)\beta(\theta) = 1.$$

But $\phi(\theta) = 0$.   Hence

$$f(\theta)\alpha(\theta) = 1.$$

The Euclidean algorithm can be used to find $\alpha(x)$.

Let us apply this method to the example λ mentioned above.   Here

$$f(x) = 3x^2 - 4x + 7$$

and

$$\phi(x) = x^3 - 5$$

is the defining equation.   By the Euclidean algorithm,

$$x^3 - 5 = \left(\frac{1}{3}x + \frac{4}{9}\right)(3x^2 - 4x + 7) + \left(-\frac{5}{9}x - \frac{73}{9}\right)$$

$$3x^2 - 4x + 7 = \left(-\frac{27}{5}x + \frac{2151}{25}\right)\left(-\frac{5}{9}x - \frac{73}{9}\right) + \frac{17{,}622}{25}.$$

Hence

$$(3x^2 - 4x + 7)\alpha(x) + (x^3 - 5)\beta(x) = 1$$

where

$$\alpha(x) = \frac{-5x^2 + 73x + 109}{1958}$$

and

$$\beta(x) = \frac{15x - 239}{1958}.$$

Therefore

$$f(\theta)\alpha(\theta) = 1, \qquad \alpha(\theta) = \frac{1}{f(\theta)}$$

or

$$\frac{1}{3x^2 - 4x + 7} \equiv \frac{-5x^2 + 73x + 109}{1958} \quad \text{mod } (x^3 - 5)$$

or

$$\frac{1}{3\sqrt[3]{25} - 4\sqrt[3]{5} + 7} = \frac{-5\sqrt[3]{25} + 73\sqrt[3]{5} + 109}{1958}.$$

3.3 Linear Dependence

An important mathematical tool with applications not only in field theory but in other branches of mathematics such as matrix theory and linear differential equations is that of *linear dependence*. In the present section we shall investigate this idea in a suitably general setting.

As a preliminary example, let us suppose that we have an additive abelian group V. Then if f and g are elements in V, we know that $f + g$ is in V; there exist an identity and inverses. Now if we consider an abstract set S, it may be possible to define "multiplication" of elements in S by those in V such that the result is in V. If this be the case, we call V a *group with operators*—the operators being elements in S. To be even more concrete, consider the module V of all pairs of real numbers, or if we like of all two-dimensional vectors emanating from the origin (cf. Exercise 1.9). Clearly V *is* a module. Now let S be the field E of real numbers. Then if f is in V and a is in E we can define af in a natural fashion, that is, as a vector with the same or opposite direction as f according as $a > 0$ or $a < 0$ and whose magnitude is $|a|$ times that of f. Clearly $af \in V$. Hence V becomes a group with operators.

A special case of a group with operators is a *vector space* which is defined below. Here the operators are restricted to a field and certain additional properties are postulated.

Definition. Let V be an additive abelian group. Let $\varDelta$ be an arbitrary field. If a multiplication of elements in V by elements in $\varDelta$ can be defined such that af is an element in V for all a in $\varDelta$ and f in V; and if furthermore

$$1 \cdot f = f$$

$$(a + b)f = af + bf$$

$$(ab)f = a(bf)$$

$$a(f + g) = af + ag$$

for all f, g in V and a, b in $\varDelta$ (where 1 is the unity element of $\varDelta$); then we say V is a *vector space* over the field $\varDelta$.

Frequently we say V is a *linear vector space* over Δ. If the ground field Δ is understood (say, for example, the real or complex numbers), then we simply say V is a *vector space*. The customary terminology is to call the elements of V *vectors* and to call the elements of Δ *scalars*. It is easily verified that the ordered pairs of real numbers considered above form a vector space over the field of real numbers. In fact, more generally, the group V of all ordered n-tuples (cf. Exercise 1.9) is a vector space over the real or complex number fields. In particular, a field is a module, so we may apply any results we obtain for vector spaces to fields and superfields.

The condition $1 \cdot f = f$ in the definition of a vector space is not superfluous, for no contradiction would arise from the remaining three conditions if, for example, af were identically zero for all $a \in \Delta$ and $f \in V$.

A vector space will be a suitably general vehicle for the introduction of the notion of *linear dependence*.

Definition. Let V be a vector space over a field Δ. A set of vectors $f_1, f_2, \cdots, f_n$ in V is said to be *linearly dependent* over Δ if scalars $a_1, a_2, \ldots, a_n \in \Delta$, not all zero, exist such that

$$a_1 f_1 + a_2 f_2 + \cdots + a_n f_n = 0.$$

In the contrary case we say $f_1, f_2, \cdots, f_n$ are *linearly independent*.

If V is the vector space of all continuous functions over the real field E, then x and $3x$ are linearly dependent, since

$$(-3)x + (+1)3x = 0$$

for all x. On the other hand, x and x^2 are linearly independent. For if there existed real numbers a and b such that

$$ax + bx^2 = 0$$

for all x, then in particular

$$a + b = 0$$

and

$$2a + 4b = 0$$

where we have let $x = 1$ and $x = 2$, respectively. These two equations imply

$$a = 0, \quad b = 0$$

and hence x and x^2 are linearly independent.

If f is an arbitrary vector in a vector space V over a field Δ, then we say f is *linearly dependent on* the set $f_1, f_2, \cdots, f_n \in V$ if there exist scalars $a_i \in \Delta$ such that

$$f = a_1f_1 + a_2f_2 + \cdots + a_nf_n.$$

From the above definition it is clear that if $f_1, f_2, \cdots, f_n$ are linearly dependent, then some f_j is linearly dependent on the remaining f_i. For if $f_1, f_2, \cdots, f_n$ are linearly dependent, then there exists a relation

$$a_1f_1 + a_2f_2 + \cdots + a_nf_n = 0, \qquad a_i \in \Delta$$

where not all the a_i are zero. Let a_α be a nonzero a_i. Since Δ is a field, a_α^{-1} exists. Multiplying the above equation through by a_α^{-1}, we obtain

$$f_\alpha = -a_\alpha^{-1}a_1f_1 - a_\alpha^{-1}a_2f_2 - \cdots$$
$$- a_\alpha^{-1}a_{\alpha-1}f_{\alpha-1} - a_\alpha^{-1}a_{\alpha+1}f_{\alpha+1} - \cdots - a_\alpha^{-1}a_nf_n.$$

Hence f_α is linearly dependent on $f_1, f_2, \cdots, f_{\alpha-1}, f_{\alpha+1}, \cdots, f_n$.

A few simple theorems on linear dependence and linear independence are:

Theorem 4. If f is linearly dependent on $f_1, f_2, \cdots, f_n$ but not on $f_1, f_2, \cdots, f_{n-1}$, then f_n is linearly dependent on $f_1, f_2, \cdots, f_{n-1}, f$.

Proof: Since f is linearly dependent on $f_1, f_2, \cdots, f_n$, a relation of the form

$$f = a_1f_1 + a_2f_2 + \cdots + a_nf_n$$

must exist. In this expression, $a_n \neq 0$, for if it were equal to zero, then f would be linearly dependent on $f_1, f_2, \cdots, f_{n-1}$, which is contrary to the hypothesis. Hence if we multiply through by a_n^{-1} we obtain

$$f_n = a_n^{-1}f - a_n^{-1}a_1f_1 - \cdots - a_n^{-1}a_{n-1}f_{n-1}.$$

Theorem 5. If f is linearly dependent on $f_1, f_2, \cdots, f_n$ and if every f_i, $i = 1, 2, \cdots, n$ is linearly dependent on $g_1, g_2, \cdots, g_m$, then f is linearly dependent on $g_1, g_2, \cdots, g_m$.

Proof: By hypothesis

$$f = \sum_{i=1}^{n} a_if_i$$

and

$$f_i = \sum_{j=1}^{m} b_{ij}g_j$$

where the a_i and b_{ij} are scalars. Hence

$$f = \sum_{i=1}^{n} a_i \left(\sum_{j=1}^{m} b_{ij}g_j \right) = \sum_{j=1}^{m} \left[\sum_{i=1}^{n} a_ib_{ij} \right]g_j = \sum_{j=1}^{m} c_jg_j$$

where the c_j,

$$c_j = \sum_{i=1}^{n} a_i b_{ij}$$

are scalars.

If x, x^2 and $3x$, $x^2 - x$ are two sets of vectors in the vector space of continuous functions, then

$$x = \tfrac{1}{3}(3x) + 0(x^2 - x)$$

$$x^2 = \tfrac{1}{3}(3x) + 1 \cdot (x^2 - x)$$

and

$$3x = 3(x) + 0(x^2)$$

$$x^2 - x = -1 \cdot (x) + 1 \cdot (x^2).$$

That is, every vector of the first set is linearly dependent on every vector in the second set and conversely. In this case we say the two sets of vectors are *equivalent*. More generally,

Definition. Let V be a vector space over a field $\varDelta$. Two sets of vectors $f_1, f_2, \cdots, f_n$ and $g_1, g_2, \cdots, g_m$ are said to be *equivalent* if every g_i is linearly dependent on the f's, and every f_j is linearly dependent on the g's.

This definition leads immediately to the two following theorems.

Theorem 6. If $f_1, f_2, \cdots, f_n$ is a set of vectors in V (not all zero), then there exists a subset $f_{i_1}, f_{i_2}, \cdots, f_{i_m}$ of linearly independent vectors equivalent to $f_1, f_2, \cdots, f_n$.

Proof: We shall prove this theorem by induction on n. If $n = 1$, the theorem is trivial. Suppose, then, that it has been proved for $n = k$. We shall prove that it is also true for $n = k + 1$.

By the induction hypothesis we may assume that there exists a subset of linearly independent vectors

$$f_{i_1}, f_{i_2}, \cdots, f_{i_r}$$

equivalent to $f_1, f_2, \cdots, f_k$. If f_{k+1} is linearly independent of $f_1, f_2, \cdots, f_k$, then it is also linearly independent of $f_{i_1}, f_{i_2}, \cdots, f_{i_r}$, since these are equivalent sets of vectors (cf. Theorem 5). Hence

$$f_{i_1}, f_{i_2}, \cdots, f_{i_r}, f_{k+1}$$

form a set of linearly independent vectors equivalent to

$$f_1, f_2, \cdots, f_k, f_{k+1}.$$

In the contrary case, f_{k+1} is linearly dependent on $f_1, f_2, \cdots, f_k$ and hence on $f_{i_1}, f_{i_2}, \cdots, f_{i_r}$. Therefore

$$f_{i_1}, f_{i_2}, \cdots, f_{i_r}$$

form a set of linearly independent vectors equivalent to

$$f_1, f_2, \cdots, f_k, f_{k+1}.$$

As an example of this theorem, consider the set of vectors

$$f_1 = 3x, \qquad f_2 = 4, \qquad f_3 = 0, \qquad f_4 = 5 - 2x$$

in the vector space of continuous functions over the real field E. We assert that $g_1 = 3x$ and $g_2 = 4$ are linearly independent vectors equivalent to f_1, f_2, f_3, f_4.

It is easy to show that g_1 and g_2 are linearly independent vectors. For if they were not there would exist an a and b in E, not both zero, such that

$$a(3x) + b(4) = 0.$$

In particular,

$$a0 + 4b = 0$$

and hence $b = 0$. From the equation

$$3ax = 0$$

we conclude $a = 0$, since $x \neq 0$ and E has no divisors of zero. To show that g_1 and g_2 are equivalent to f_1, f_2, f_3, f_4 we have

$$f_1 = g_1$$
$$f_2 = g_2$$
$$f_3 = 0g_1$$
$$f_4 = \tfrac{5}{4}g_2 - \tfrac{2}{3}g_1.$$

Since g_1 and g_2 are a subset of the f_i, clearly they are linearly dependent on the f_i.

Theorem 7. Let V be a vector space over a field Δ. Let $f_1, f_2, \cdots, f_n$ be a set of linearly independent vectors in V. Let $g_1, g_2, \cdots, g_m$ be a set of vectors in V upon which every f_i is linearly dependent. Then among the m vectors $g_1, g_2, \cdots, g_m$ there exists a subset of $m - n$ vectors

$$g_{i_{n+1}}, g_{i_{n+2}}, \cdots, g_{i_m}$$

such that the two systems

$$f_1, f_2, \cdots, f_n, g_{t_{n+1}}, g_{t_{n+2}}, \cdots, g_{t_m}$$

and

$$g_1, g_2, \cdots, g_m$$

are equivalent.

Proof: The proof of this theorem will be by induction on α, the number of linearly independent vectors. If $\beta = 0$, the theorem is trivial. Assume, then, that the theorem has been proved for $\beta = 1, 2, \cdots, k$. We shall show that it is true for $\beta = k + 1$.

By the induction hypothesis there exist vectors g_{t_r} such that the two systems

$$f_1, f_2, \cdots, f_k, g_{t_{k+1}}, g_{t_{k+2}}, \cdots, g_{t_m} \tag{3.3}$$

and

$$g_1, g_2, \cdots, g_m$$

are equivalent. Consider the vector f_{k+1}. By hypothesis, f_{k+1} is linearly dependent on either set of vectors. Hence, in particular, there exist scalars a_j in Δ such that

$$f_{k+1} = a_1 f_1 + a_2 f_2 + \cdots + a_k f_k + a_{k+1} g_{t_{k+1}} + \cdots + a_m g_{t_m}. \tag{3.4}$$

Since $f_1, f_2, \cdots, f_{k+1}$ are linearly independent by hypothesis, not all the $a_j, j > k$ are zero. Suppose $a_\alpha, \alpha \geq k + 1$ is not zero. Then if we multiply the above equation through by a_α^{-1} and solve for g_{t_α} we obtain

$$g_{t_\alpha} = a_\alpha^{-1} f_{k+1} - a_\alpha^{-1} a_1 f_1 - \cdots - a_\alpha^{-1} a_k f_k - a_\alpha^{-1} a_{k+1} g_{t_{k+1}} - \cdots$$
$$- a_\alpha^{-1} a_{\alpha-1} g_{t_{\alpha-1}} - a_\alpha^{-1} a_{\alpha+1} g_{t_{\alpha+1}} - \cdots - a_\alpha^{-1} a_m g_{t_m}. \tag{3.5}$$

From Equations 3.4 and 3.5 we conclude that the two systems

$$f_1, f_2, \cdots, f_k, f_{k+1}, g_{t_{k+1}}, \cdots, g_{t_{\alpha-1}}, g_{t_{\alpha+1}}, \cdots, g_{t_m} \tag{3.6}$$

and

$$f_1, f_2, \cdots, f_k, g_{t_{k+1}}, g_{t_{k+2}}, \cdots, g_{t_m}$$

are equivalent; since every vector of either set is linearly dependent on the vectors of the other set. By Theorem 5, the set of vectors of Equation 3.6 is equivalent to $g_1, g_2, \cdots, g_m$ and hence our theorem is proved.

This last theorem is known as the *Steinitz exchange principle* or the *interchange* theorem. An immediate corollary is:

Theorem 8. If $f_1, f_2, \cdots, f_n$ and $g_1, g_2, \cdots, g_m$ are two sets of linearly independent vectors which are equivalent, then $n = m$.

Having mentioned a few of the more important elementary theorems on linear dependence we return to a study of field theory. In our definition óf a vector space, V was a module. As remarked above, a field is a module and hence the above theorems on linear dependence can be applied to fields and superfields, where the elements of the superfield are the vectors and those of the field are the scalars. We start with a more general definition.

Definition. Let V be a vector space over a field $\varDelta$. Suppose that there exists a finite set of linearly independent vectors $f_1, f_2, \cdots, f_n$ such that every vector of V is linearly dependent on these n vectors. Then the set $f_1, f_2, \cdots, f_n$ is called a *basis* for V. In particular we say V has a *finite basis*. The number of elements in a basis is called the *rank* of V over $\varDelta$ and is denoted by the symbol $(V:\varDelta)$. The number $(V:\varDelta)$ is often called the *dimension* of the vector space.

For example, in the vector space V of all ordered pairs of real numbers over the real field E, the vectors $\{1,0\}$ and $\{0,1\}$ form a basis. First $\{1,0\}$ and $\{0,1\}$ are linearly independent. For suppose scalars a and b (elements of E) existed such that

$$a\{1,0\} + b\{0,1\} = \{0,0\}.$$

Then

$$\{a,b\} = \{0,0\}$$

would imply

$$a = 0, \qquad b = 0.$$

Now let $\{\alpha,\beta\}$ be an arbitrary vector in V. Then

$$\{\alpha,\beta\} = \alpha\{1,0\} + \beta\{0,1\}$$

and every vector is linearly dependent on $\{1,0\}$ and $\{0,1\}$. Hence the vectors $\{1,0\}$ and $\{0,1\}$ form a basis for V and $(V:E) = 2$, that is, the dimension of V over E is two.

The dimension of a vector space is unique. For suppose $f_1, f_2, \cdots,$ f_n and $g_1, g_2, \cdots, g_m$ are two linearly independent sets of vectors in V which are both bases. Then in particular, every f_i would be linearly dependent on the g's and every g_j would be linearly dependent on the f's. Hence the f's and g's would be equivalent sets of vectors. By Theorem 8, we conclude that $n = m$ and hence the dimension of the vector space is unique.

Also the representation of a vector in terms of a basis is unique. For suppose V is a vector space over a field $\varDelta$ and $f_1, f_2, \cdots, f_n$ are a basis in V. Then if f is any vector in V, it has a representation

$$f = a_1f_1 + a_2f_2 + \cdots + a_nf_n$$

where the a_i are in Δ. We assert that this characterization is unique. For suppose

$$f = b_1 f_1 + b_2 f_2 + \cdots + b_n f_n, \qquad b_i \in \Delta,$$

then on subtracting these two equations,

$$0 = (a_1 - b_1)f_1 + (a_2 - b_2)f_2 + \cdots + (a_n - b_n)f_n.$$

Since the f_i are linearly independent, this implies

$$a_i - b_i = 0$$

or

$$a_i = b_i, \qquad i = 1, 2, \cdots, n$$

and the representation of f in terms of the basis is unique.

As a special case, V could be a field. Suppose, then, that Δ is a field and θ is an element which is algebraic over Δ. Then we can consider the field $\Delta(\theta)$ as a vector space over Δ. The reader may readily verify this conclusion. From Theorem 3 we know there exists a polynomial $\phi(x) \in \Delta[x]$ of minimal degree (that is, the defining polynomial) which has θ as a root, $\phi(\theta) = 0$ in $\Delta(\theta)$. Let n be the degree of ϕ. Now, again from Theorem 3,

$$\Delta[\theta] = \Delta(\theta) \approx \Delta[x]/(\phi(x)).$$

Hence every element of $\Delta(\theta)$ (that is, every rational function of θ) can be expressed as a polynomial in θ with elements in Δ as coefficients. Furthermore, any such polynomial must be of degree at most $n - 1$ since a polynomial of arbitrary degree is congruent modulo $(\phi(x))$ to a polynomial of degree less than n. Therefore every element in $\Delta(\theta)$ can be expressed in the form

$$c_0 \theta^{n-1} + c_1 \theta^{n-2} + \cdots + c_{n-1}, \qquad c_i \in \Delta.$$

We assert that the elements $1, \theta, \theta^2, \cdots, \theta^{n-1}$ form a basis for the vector space $\Delta(\theta)$ over Δ. By our above discussion, every element in $\Delta(\theta)$ is linearly dependent on $1, \theta, \theta^2, \cdots, \theta^{n-1}$. The elements $1, \theta, \theta^2, \cdots, \theta^{n-1}$ are *linearly independent*. For if they were not, the defining polynomial $\phi(x)$ would be of degree less than n since θ^{n-1} could then be replaced by a linear combination of $1, \theta, \cdots, \theta^{n-2}$ with coefficients in Δ. We see, therefore, that the rank of $\Delta(\theta)$ over Δ is n,

$$n = (\Delta(\theta):\Delta),$$

that is, the dimension of the vector space $\Delta(\theta)$ over the field Δ is equal to the degree of the defining equation. An earlier result establishes the uniqueness of n.

A superfield Ξ over a field $\varDelta$ is said to be a *finite extension* of $\varDelta$ if the rank of Ξ over $\varDelta$ is finite. This definition is in harmony with the above discussion; in particular, $\varDelta(\theta)$ is a finite extension of $\varDelta$. We shall show later (Theorem 11) that every finite extension of $\varDelta$ may be obtained by the adjunction of finitely many algebraic elements to $\varDelta$.

Using the concept of linear dependence we can easily prove the result that if θ is algebraic over $\varDelta$, then every element $f(\theta) \in \varDelta(\theta)$ is also algebraic over $\varDelta$, that is $f(\theta)$ satisfies a polynomial equation

$$c_0 f^n + c_1 f^{n-1} + \cdots + c_n = 0, \qquad c_i \in \varDelta.$$

Proof: Consider the elements

$$1, f, f^2, \cdots, f^n$$

in $\varDelta(\theta)$. They must be linearly dependent, for if they were not, the dimension of $\varDelta(\theta)$ over $\varDelta$ would be greater than or equal to $n + 1$. But $(\varDelta(\theta):\varDelta) = n$ and this number n is unique. Hence the vectors $1, f, f^2, \cdots, f^n$ are linearly dependent and therefore there exist scalars (elements in $\varDelta$) such that

$$c_n + c_{n-1} f + \cdots + c_0 f^n = 0.$$

A simple property of the rank of a superfield over a given field is expressed in the following theorem.

Theorem 9. Let $\varDelta_1$, $\varDelta_2$, and $\varDelta_3$ be fields such that $\varDelta_1 \subseteq \varDelta_2 \subseteq \varDelta_3$ and the rank of $\varDelta_{i+1}$ over $\varDelta_i$ is finite, $i = 1, 2$. Then the rank of $\varDelta_3$ over $\varDelta_1$ is equal to the product of the rank of $\varDelta_3$ over $\varDelta_2$ by the rank of $\varDelta_2$ over $\varDelta_1$. In symbols,

$$(\varDelta_3:\varDelta_1) = (\varDelta_3:\varDelta_2)(\varDelta_2:\varDelta_1).$$

Proof: Let $\alpha_1, \alpha_2, \cdots, \alpha_n$ be a basis in $\varDelta_2$ considered as a vector space over $\varDelta_1$. Then $n = (\varDelta_2:\varDelta_1)$. Let $\beta_1, \beta_2, \cdots, \beta_m$ be a basis in $\varDelta_3$ considered as a vector space over $\varDelta_2$. Then $m = (\varDelta_3:\varDelta_2)$. Now let θ be an arbitrary element in $\varDelta_3$:

$$\theta = \sum_{i=1}^{m} \lambda_i \beta_i, \qquad \lambda_i \in \varDelta_2.$$

Also,

$$\lambda_i = \sum_{j=1}^{n} b_{ij} \alpha_j, \qquad b_{ij} \in \varDelta_1.$$

Combining these two equations,

$$\theta = \sum_{i=1}^{m} \sum_{j=1}^{n} b_{ij}(\alpha_j \beta_i).$$

Hence every element θ in Δ_3 is linearly dependent on the mn quantities $\alpha_j\beta_i, j = 1, 2, \cdots, n, i = 1, 2, \cdots, m$ with coefficients b_{ij} in Δ_1. To prove that $(\Delta_3 : \Delta_1) = mn$ we must show that the $\alpha_j\beta_i$ are linearly independent. Suppose the contrary. Then there exists a relation

$$\sum_{j,\,i} c_{ji}\alpha_j\beta_i = 0$$

with the $c_{ji} \in \Delta_1$ not all zero. We shall obtain the contradiction that the c_{ji} must be zero and hence that the $\alpha_j\beta_i$ are mn independent quantities. Now the β_i are linearly independent over Δ_2. Hence the coefficients of every β_i, namely,

$$\sum_{j} c_{ji}\alpha_j$$

must be zero. But the α_j are linearly independent over Δ_1, and therefore each c_{ji} must be zero.

Other simple theorems and corollaries of this theorem will be left as exercises for the reader. (Cf. the exercises at the end of this chapter.) Note that the λ_i of the theorem are *vectors* when Δ_2 is considered as a vector space over Δ_1, but are *scalars* when Δ_3 is considered as a vector space over Δ_2.

3.4 Algebraic Field Extensions

In the discussion following Theorem 3 we said that an element θ was *algebraic* over a field Δ if there existed a polynomial $\phi(x) \in \Delta[x]$ with the property that $\phi(\theta) = 0$ in $\Delta(\theta)$. A natural extension of this definition is:

Definition. Let Δ be a field and Ξ a superfield over Δ, that is, $\Delta \subseteq \Xi$. Then if every element of Ξ is algebraic over Δ we say that the *field Ξ is algebraic over Δ.*

From the previous section we see that if θ is algebraic over Δ, then $\Delta(\theta)$ is algebraic over Δ, since every element $f(\theta)$ in $\Delta(\theta)$ is algebraic over Δ. Hence a field $\Delta(\theta)$, which is a simple algebraic extension of a field Δ, is algebraic over Δ. In general we can show that if Ω is an algebraic extension of Δ, that is, a field obtained from Δ by adjoining algebraic elements to Δ, then Ω is algebraic over Δ.

In our fundamental definition of field adjunctions in Section 3.2 we considered a field Δ contained in some superfield Ξ and generated the field $\Delta(M)$, where M was an arbitrary set of elements of Ξ. If we desire we can adjoin only a finite number of elements of M, say $\{\alpha_1, \alpha_2, \cdots, \alpha_n\}$. This field $\Delta(\alpha_1, \alpha_2, \cdots, \alpha_n)$ is the same as the field $\Delta(\alpha_1)(\alpha_2) \cdots (\alpha_n)$ which consists of a *finite* number of simple field

adjunctions.   In our work we have defined *finite extensions* (if the rank
of the extension field over Δ were finite); an *element algebraic over Δ* and
an extension *field algebraic over Δ*.   In the next few theorems we wish
to show various relations that exist among these definitions.

We note that a simple field adjunction of a field Δ is not necessarily
a finite extension, for example, if x is an indeterminate, then $\Delta(x)$ is
not a finite extension.   However, if x is *algebraic*, then $(\Delta(x):\Delta)$ *is*
finite.   In general, then, we have the following theorem.

Theorem 10.   Let Δ be a field and let $\alpha_1, \alpha_2, \cdots, \alpha_n$ be n elements
algebraic over Δ.   (Both Δ and $\alpha_1, \alpha_2, \cdots, \alpha_n$ are in some superfield
Ξ.)   Then the rank of $\Delta(\alpha_1, \alpha_2, \cdots, \alpha_n)$ over Δ is finite, that is
$\Delta(\alpha_1, \alpha_2, \cdots, \alpha_n)$ is a finite extension of Δ.

Proof: We have

$$\Delta \subseteq \Delta(\alpha_1) \subseteq \Delta(\alpha_1, \alpha_2) \subseteq \cdots \subseteq \Delta(\alpha_1, \alpha_2, \cdots, \alpha_n).$$

Now since α_k is algebraic over Δ, it is certainly algebraic over
$\Delta(\alpha_1, \alpha_2, \cdots, \alpha_{k-1})$.   Hence the dimension of $\Delta(\alpha_1, \alpha_2, \cdots, \alpha_{k-1}, \alpha_k) =$
$\Delta(\alpha_1, \alpha_2, \cdots, \alpha_{k-1})(\alpha_k)$ over $\Delta(\alpha_1, \alpha_2, \cdots, \alpha_{k-1})$ is finite, say λ_k.   By
Theorem 9,

$$(\Delta(\alpha_1, \alpha_2, \cdots, \alpha_n):\Delta) = \lambda_1 \lambda_2 \ldots \lambda_n$$

which is finite.

The above theorem shows a relation between algebraic elements and
finite extensions, that is, every field Ω obtained from a given field Δ by
the adjunction of finitely many algebraic elements is a finite extension
of Δ.   We leave as an exercise for the reader the proof of the statement:
"If $\alpha_1, \alpha_2, \cdots, \alpha_n$ are algebraic over Δ, then $\Delta(\alpha_1, \alpha_2, \cdots, \alpha_n)$ is
algebraic over Δ."

A converse of Theorem 10 is:

Theorem 11.   Every finite extension Ω of a field Δ is algebraic and
may be obtained from Δ by the adjunction of finitely many algebraic
elements.

Proof: If $(\Omega:\Delta) = 1$, then $\Omega = \Delta$ and the theorem is trivial.   Let
then $n = (\Omega:\Delta) > 1$ and let θ be an arbitrary element in Ω not in Δ.
Then among the $n + 1$ elements

$$1, \theta, \theta^2, \cdots, \theta^n$$

in Ω there are at most n linearly independent ones, for if there were more, the rank of $\varDelta(\theta) \subseteq \Omega$ over $\varDelta$ would be greater than n, which is a contradiction. Hence there exists a relation

$$\sum_{k=0}^{n} c_k \theta^k = 0, \qquad c_k \in \varDelta$$

with the c_k not all zero. (This shows that Ω is algebraic over $\varDelta$ by the very definition.) Now

$$\varDelta \subset \varDelta(\theta) \subseteq \Omega$$

and

$$n = (\Omega:\varDelta) = (\Omega:\varDelta(\theta))(\varDelta(\theta):\varDelta).$$

If $(\varDelta(\theta):\varDelta) = n$, then $(\Omega:\varDelta(\theta)) = 1$ and our theorem is proved. If not, suppose

$$(\varDelta(\theta):\varDelta) = m < n.$$

Since $\theta \notin \varDelta$, $m > 1$. Choose an element ζ in Ω not in $\varDelta(\theta)$. Then we can show as above that ζ is algebraic over $\varDelta$ and

$$(\varDelta(\theta,\zeta):\varDelta) = p$$

where

$$p > m.$$

If $p = \dot{} n$, then $\varDelta(\theta,\zeta) = \Omega$ and our theorem is proved. If not, we may continue this process a finite number of times until

$$(\varDelta(\theta, \zeta, \cdots, \omega):\varDelta) = n.$$

Then

$$n = (\Omega:\varDelta) = (\Omega:\varDelta(\theta, \zeta, \cdots, \omega))(\varDelta(\theta, \zeta, \cdots, \omega):\varDelta)$$

and

$$(\Omega:\varDelta(\theta, \zeta, \cdots, \omega)) = 1$$

or

$$\Omega = \varDelta(\theta, \zeta, \cdots, \omega)$$

where $\theta, \zeta, \cdots, \omega$ are algebraic over $\varDelta$.

If $\varDelta_1 \subseteq \varDelta_2 \subseteq \varDelta_3$ are three fields with $\varDelta_{i+1}$ algebraic over $\varDelta_i$, $i = 1, 2$, then we leave it to the reader to show that $\varDelta_3$ is algebraic over $\varDelta_1$. We prove an analogous result using two fields and an element rather than three fields.

Theorem 12. If θ is an element algebraic over a field $\varXi$ and $\varXi$ is algebraic over $\varDelta$, then θ is algebraic over $\varDelta$.

Proof: Since θ is algebraic over Ξ, it satisfies a polynomial equation

$$\sum_{k=0}^{n} \alpha_k \theta^k = 0$$

where the coefficients α_k (not all zero) are in Ξ. Since Ξ is algebraic over $\varDelta$, each α_i satisfies an equation

$$\sum_j a_{kj}\alpha_k^j = 0$$

with the a_{kj} in $\varDelta$ and not all zero.

Now by Theorem 10, $\varDelta(\alpha_0, \alpha_1, \cdots, \alpha_n)$ is of finite rank over $\varDelta$ and by the above construction $\varDelta(\alpha_0, \alpha_1, \cdots, \alpha_n)(\theta)$ is of finite rank over $\varDelta(\alpha_0, \alpha_1, \cdots, \alpha_n)$. By Theorem 9, $\varDelta(\alpha_0, \alpha_1, \cdots, \alpha_n, \theta)$ is of finite rank over $\varDelta$ and finally, by Theorem 11, θ is algebraic over $\varDelta$. This completes the proof.

In many of the previous discussions we have been using algebraic extensions of a field $\varDelta$ other than simple algebraic extensions. That is, we have considered fields $\varDelta(\alpha_1, \alpha_2, \cdots, \alpha_n)$ obtained from $\varDelta$ by the adjunction of the algebraic elements $\alpha_1, \alpha_2, \cdots, \alpha_n$. Various properties of such fields have been proved in previous theorems. We know, for example, that if α and β are algebraic over $\varDelta$, then $\alpha\beta$ and $\alpha \pm \beta$ are also algebraic over $\varDelta$. This leads us to consider the following problem: Is it possible to find a single algebraic element θ such that $\varDelta(\alpha,\beta) = \varDelta(\theta)$? That is, can a finite algebraic extension of a field always be written as a *simple* algebraic extension? Conditions under which this is true are found in the important "theorem of the primitive element". (Cf. Theorem 13.)

Before proving this theorem, we consider an example. Let K be the field of rational numbers and let $\sqrt{2}$ and $\sqrt{3}$ be adjoined to K:

$$K(\sqrt{2}, \sqrt{3}).$$

Both K and $\sqrt{2}$, $\sqrt{3}$ can be considered as belonging to the superfield Ξ of real numbers. The elements $\sqrt{2}$ and $\sqrt{3}$ are algebraic over K. Their defining equations are

$$f(x) = x^2 - 2 = 0$$

and

$$g(x) = x^2 - 3 = 0$$

respectively. We assert that there exists an algebraic element θ such that

$$K(\sqrt{2}, \sqrt{3}) = K(\theta).$$

In fact, $\theta = \sqrt{2} + \sqrt{3}$ is such an element.

Certainly,

$$K(\sqrt{2} + \sqrt{3}) \subseteq K(\sqrt{2}, \sqrt{3}).$$

We shall now prove the converse. Since $K(\sqrt{2} + \sqrt{3})$ is a field,

$$(\sqrt{2} + \sqrt{3})^3 = 11\sqrt{2} + 9\sqrt{3}$$

as well as

$$- 9(\sqrt{2} + \sqrt{3})$$

are elements of the field. The sum of these two elements is $2\sqrt{2}$, and since $\frac{1}{2} \in K$, the element $\sqrt{2}$ is in $K(\sqrt{2} + \sqrt{3})$. Hence $(\sqrt{2} + \sqrt{3}) - \sqrt{2} = \sqrt{3}$ is also in $K(\sqrt{2} + \sqrt{3})$ and therefore $K(\sqrt{2} + \sqrt{3}) \supseteq K(\sqrt{2}, \sqrt{3})$. This proves the statement

$$K(\sqrt{2}, \sqrt{3}) = K(\sqrt{2} + \sqrt{3}).$$

The defining polynomial for $\theta = \sqrt{2} + \sqrt{3}$ is

$$f(x) = x^4 - 10x^2 + 1 \in K[x]$$

since

$$\theta^2 = 5 + 2\sqrt{6}$$

$$\theta^4 = 49 + 20\sqrt{6}$$

and

$$\theta^4 - 10\theta^2 = - 1.$$

No equation of lower degree has θ as a root. This can be seen as follows. Let $L = K(\sqrt{2})$. Then clearly

$$(L : K) = 2$$

and

$$(L(\sqrt{3}) : L) = 2.$$

Thus by Theorem 9,

$$(L(\sqrt{3}) : K) = 4.$$

But

$$L(\sqrt{3}) = K(\sqrt{2})(\sqrt{3}) = K(\sqrt{2}, \sqrt{3}) = K(\theta),$$

and we have seen earlier that the rank of $K(\theta)$ over K is equal to the degree of the defining polynomial.

Definition Let Δ be a field and let θ be an element algebraic over Δ. If the defining equation for $\Delta(\theta)$ has θ as a *simple* zero, then θ is said to be *separable*.

In a field of characteristic zero, this is always the case as may readily be verified by the reader. We now state and prove the fundamental theorem known as the "theorem of the primitive element."

Theorem 13. If Δ is a field which has an infinite number of elements, and if α and β are algebraic over Δ with β separable, then there exists an element θ in $\Delta(\alpha,\beta)$ such that $\Delta(\alpha,\beta) = \Delta(\theta)$. (Of course Δ, α and β, and θ are all contained in some superfield Ξ.)

Proof: Let $f(x)$ and $g(x)$ be the defining polynomials for $\Delta(\alpha)$ and $\Delta(\beta)$, respectively. Then $f(\alpha) = 0$ in $\Delta(\alpha)$ and $g(\beta) = 0$ in $\Delta(\beta)$. Let $f(x)$ be of degree m with zeros

$$\alpha, \alpha_2, \cdots, \alpha_m$$

and $g(x)$ be of degree n with zeros

$$\beta, \beta_2, \cdots, \beta_n.$$

(The zeros $\alpha_2, \cdots, \alpha_m$ and $\beta_2, \cdots, \beta_n$ lie in some extension field of Δ, say Ξ.)

Consider now the expression

$$\theta = \alpha + c\beta \in \Delta(\alpha,\beta)$$

where the element $c \in \Delta$ is so chosen that

$$\alpha_i + c\beta_j \neq \alpha + c\beta \qquad \begin{array}{l} i = 2, 3, \cdots, m \\ j = 2, 3, \cdots, n. \end{array}$$

This is possible since by hypothesis Δ contains an infinite number of elements and β is separable. Let $\Delta(\theta)[x]$ be the ring of polynomials over the field $\Delta(\theta)$. Both $g(x) \in \Delta(\theta)[x]$ and $f(\theta - cx) \in \Delta(\theta)[x]$ have β as a zero in $\Delta(\alpha,\beta)$. By Theorem 20 of Chapter 2 we know that $\Delta(\theta)[x]$ is a Euclidean ring. Hence by Theorem 27, let $h(x)$ be a G.C.D. of $g(x)$ and $f(\theta - cx)$,

$$h(x) = r(x)g(x) + s(x)f(\theta - cx) \qquad r, s \in \Delta(\theta)[x].$$

Now $g(\beta) = f(\theta - c\beta) = 0$; hence β is a zero of $h(x)$. Furthermore, $g(x)$ and $f(\theta - cx)$ have no other common zero. For the other zeros (in Ξ) of $g(x)$ are $\beta_2, \cdots, \beta_m$ and $f(\theta - c\beta_j) \neq 0, j = 2, \cdots, m$ by our choice of c. Therefore the only zero of $h(x)$ is β. Since β is separable in Δ it is certainly separable over $\Delta(\theta)$ and hence $h(x)$ is of degree one:

$$h(x) = x - \beta \in \Delta(\theta)[x].$$

Therefore $\beta \in \Delta(\theta)$. But $\alpha = \theta - c\beta$ and $c \in \Delta$. Hence α is also in $\Delta(\theta)$ and we have $\Delta(\alpha,\beta) \subseteq \Delta(\theta)$. Clearly $\Delta(\theta) \subseteq \Delta(\alpha,\beta)$ since $\theta = \alpha + c\beta$ and therefore $\Delta(\theta) = \Delta(\alpha,\beta)$.

As a corollary, we note that if Δ is a field of characteristic zero and

$\alpha_1, \alpha_2, \cdots, \alpha_n$ are algebraic over Δ, then there exists an algebraic element θ such that

$$\Delta(\alpha_1, \alpha_2, \cdots, \alpha_n) = \Delta(\theta).$$

In the proof of the above theorem we considered the defining polynomial $f(x)$ of $\Delta(\alpha)$ which had the property that $f(\alpha) = 0$ in $\Delta(\alpha)$. Of course $f(x)$ has other zeros $\alpha_2, \cdots, \alpha_n$ in some extension field, say Ξ. It may be that Ξ coincides with $\Delta(\alpha)$; however, this is not the general situation. For example, if K is the field of rational numbers, then $x^3 - 2 \in K[x]$ is the defining polynomial for $K(\sqrt[3]{2})$. But the other roots of $x^3 - 2 = 0$, namely $\dfrac{\sqrt[3]{2}}{2}(-1 \pm i\sqrt{3})$ are *not* in $K(\sqrt[3]{2})$. However, if we adjoin the cube root of unity $\omega = -\dfrac{1}{2} + \dfrac{i\sqrt{3}}{2}$ to $K(\sqrt[3]{2})$, then in the field $K(\sqrt[3]{2}, \omega)$, we can completely factor $x^3 - 2$, that is, all the roots of $x^3 - 2 = 0$ lie in this field. Such a field is called a *splitting field*. More generally,

Definition. If Ω is the smallest extension field of a field Δ such that $f(x) \in \Delta[x]$ factors completely in Ω, then we shall call Ω the *splitting field* of $f(x)$ over Δ.

The existence of such a field may be shown by the repeated construction of fields like the field $\Delta[x]/N$ of Theorem 3.

If Δ is a field and Ω is the splitting field of $f(x)$ over Δ, it is, of course, possible that $\Delta = \Omega$. For example, the splitting field of $x^2 - 5x + 6 \in K[x]$ is K. However, as seen above, this is not the general situation for an arbitrary $f(x)$ in $K[x]$. Is it then possible to determine an extension field Ω of a given field Δ such that Ω is the splitting field of every polynomial $f(x)$ in $\Omega[x]$? We know, for example, that the field of complex numbers C has this property. That is, if $f(x)$ is any polynomial in $C[x]$, then all the roots of $f(x) = 0$ are again complex numbers and hence lie in C. A field with this property is called *algebraically closed*. The rational and real fields, K and E, are not closed, since, for example, $x^2 + 1$ is in $K[x]$ and in $E[x]$, yet $i \notin K, i \notin E$.

In the Appendix we prove the important result that every field Δ has an algebraically closed algebraic extension which is unique up to isomorphisms over Δ. The proof of this theorem necessitates certain rather involved set theoretic preliminaries which are also discussed in the Appendix.

Our proof of this theorem in the Appendix requires the use of certain properties of *continuations of isomorphisms*. We are in a position to prove the necessary results at the present stage of our development.

Definition.   Let $\varDelta$ and $\varDelta'$ be two isomorphic fields and let $\varXi$ and $\varXi'$ be extension fields of $\varDelta$ and $\varDelta'$, respectively.   An isomorphism $\chi:\varXi\leftrightarrow\varXi'$ is called a *continuation* of the isomorphism $\psi:\varDelta\leftrightarrow\varDelta'$ if $\chi(a) = \psi(a)$ for all a in $\varDelta$.

Theorem 14.   Let $\varDelta$ and $\varDelta'$ be two isomorphic fields.   Let $f(x)$ be an irreducible polynomial in $\varDelta[x]$ which is mapped onto the (also irreducible) polynomial $f'(x)$ in $\varDelta'[x]$.   If α is a zero of $f(x)$ in some extension field of $\varDelta$, and α' is a zero of $f'(x)$ in some extension field of $\varDelta'$, then the given isomorphism $\varDelta\approx\varDelta'$ may be continued into an isomorphism $\varDelta(\alpha)\approx\varDelta'(\alpha')$ in which α is mapped onto α'.

Proof: Since $f(x) = 0$ is the defining equation for $\varDelta(\alpha)$, we have $\varDelta(\alpha)\approx\varDelta[x]/(f(x))$ by Theorem 3.   Hence every element $g(\alpha)$ in $\varDelta(\alpha)$ may be written as a polynomial $\sum c_k\alpha^k$ of degree less than that of $f(x)$ with coefficients in $\varDelta$.   Similarly $\varDelta'(\alpha')\approx\varDelta'[x]/(f'(x))$.   Establish a mapping

$$\chi:\qquad \sum c_k\alpha^k \to \sum c_k'\alpha'^k$$

of $\varDelta(\alpha)$ onto $\varDelta'(\alpha')$ where $\psi(c_k) = c_k'$, ψ being the isomorphism, $\psi:\varDelta\leftrightarrow\varDelta'$.   The mapping χ is one to one, since the degree of f' is the same as f and hence every element $g'(\alpha')$ in $\varDelta'(\alpha')$ may be written as a polynomial $\sum c_k'\alpha'^k$ of degree less than that of f with coefficients c_k' in $\varDelta'$. By definition of addition and multiplication of polynomials, χ is an isomorphism.   Clearly it is a continuation of ψ.

As an example, let $\varDelta = \varDelta' = K$, the field of rational numbers.   Let $f(x) = x^2 + 1$ and $f'(x) = x^2 + 1$ in $\varDelta[x]$ and $\varDelta'[x]$, respectively. Furthermore, let $\alpha = i$ and $\alpha' = -i$.   Then from the above theorem we conclude

$$K(i) \approx K(-i)$$

where i is mapped onto $-i$ under the above isomorphism.   That is, the isomorphism maps a complex number on its conjugate.   Isomorphisms of this type are called *automorphisms*, that is, an isomorphism which maps a set onto itself is called an automorphism.   [Clearly $K(i)$ and $K(-i)$ both contain the same elements.]

We could, of course, have mapped i onto i.   Then the automorphism $K(i)\approx K(-i)$ would have been the identity automorphism.   In general, if $\varDelta$ is a field and $f(x)$ is the defining polynomial of degree n for $\varDelta(\theta)$ we can consider the automorphisms

$$\varDelta(\theta_1, \theta_2, \cdots, \theta_n) \approx \varDelta(\theta_{t_1}, \theta_{t_2}, \cdots, \theta_{t_n})$$

where $\theta = \theta_1$ and $\theta_2, \theta_3, \cdots, \theta_n$ are the n zeros of $f(x)$ in its splitting field.

If we return to Theorem 14 we recall that the isomorphism $\varDelta\approx\varDelta'$

was continued to the isomorphism $\Delta(\alpha) \approx \Delta'(\alpha')$. However, every isomorphism of $\Delta(\alpha)$ and $\Delta'(\alpha')$ in which α goes into α' is not necessarily a *continuation* of the given isomorphism. For example, let Γ be the quotient field of the Gaussian integers, that is $\Gamma = K(i)$, where K is the rational field. Let, according to Theorem 14, $\Delta = \Delta' = \Gamma$ and let

$$\Gamma \approx \Gamma$$

under the mapping $\beta \leftrightarrow \bar{\beta}$. That is, we have an automorphism in which every number β in Γ is mapped onto its conjugate $\bar{\beta}$ (also in Γ). Then if we consider

$$f(x) = x^2 - 2 \in \Gamma[x]$$

and let $\alpha = \sqrt{2}$, $\alpha' = -\sqrt{2}$, the isomorphism

$$\Gamma(\alpha) \approx \Gamma(\alpha')$$

is either a continuation of the original isomorphism (if $\beta \in \Gamma$ goes into $\bar{\beta}$) or it can be a new isomorphism in which $\beta \leftrightarrow \beta$ if $\beta \in \Gamma$ and $\alpha \leftrightarrow \alpha'$. We could, of course, consider this new isomorphism as a continuation of the identity isomorphism $\Gamma \approx \Gamma$ which maps every β in Γ onto β.

3.5 The Structure of Finite Fields

In Section 3.1. we considered fields of characteristic p, for example, the ring $Z/(2)$ of remainder classes modulo 2 of the ring of integers Z is a field of characteristic two. All fields of characteristic p do not necessarily contain a finite number of elements. For example, the simple transcendental extension $Z/(2)(x)$ of $Z/(2)$ is a field of characteristic two with an infinite number of elements. When a field *does* contain a finite number of elements we shall call it a *finite field* or a *Galois field*. It is the purpose of the present section to discuss and prove certain elementary properties of such fields.

Let us suppose then that F is a finite field, distinct from the null field, containing q elements. Of necessity, q is greater than one. If we consider the intersection of all subfields of F we obtain its prime field Π. By Theorem 1 of Section 3.1 we know that Π is either isomorphic to the field K of rational numbers or

$$\Pi \approx Z/(p)$$

where p is a prime number in the ring of integers Z. Since F has only a finite number of elements, Π can have only a finite number and the possibility that Π is isomorphic to K must be rejected. The only other alternative is that Π is isomorphic to $Z/(p)$ and hence is a field of characteristic p. Our first problem will be to determine the form of q, the number of elements of F.

Since F is a superfield over Π, we may consider it as a vector space over Π. Let $n = (F:\Pi)$ be the dimension of F over Π. Clearly n is finite. We assert that $q = p^n$.

Theorem 15. Let F be a finite field and Π its prime field. Then the number of elements q in the field F is equal to p^n, where n is the rank of F over Π, and p is the characteristic of F.

Proof: Since $n = (F:\Pi)$ is finite, the field F considered as a vector space over Π has a finite basis, say

$$\zeta_1, \zeta_2, \cdots, \zeta_n.$$

Hence every element λ in F can be expressed as a linear combination of the ζ_i's with coefficients in Π:

$$\lambda = a_1\zeta_1 + a_2\zeta_2 + \cdots + a_n\zeta_n, \qquad a_i \in \Pi.$$

Now in any expression

$$b_1\zeta_1 + b_2\zeta_2 + \cdots + b_n\zeta_n, \qquad b_j \in \Pi = Z/(p)$$

there are p distinct values which the b_j's may assume, since there are p distinct elements in $\Pi = Z/(p)$. Hence there are at most p^n elements in F. We assert that there are precisely p^n distinct elements in F. For suppose

$$b_1\zeta_1 + b_2\zeta_2 + \cdots + b_n\zeta_n = c_1\zeta_1 + c_2\zeta_2 + \cdots + c_n\zeta_n$$

and not every $b_j - c_j = 0$. Then subtracting,

$$(b_1 - c_1)\zeta_1 + (b_2 - c_2)\zeta_2 + \cdots + (b_n - c_n)\zeta_n = 0.$$

Now not every $b_j - c_j = 0$. Hence the ζ_j are linearly dependent. But the ζ_j form a basis in F over Π and hence are linearly independent. The contradiction proves the assertion.

In Section 3.1. we considered the field $G/(3)$, where G was the ring of Gaussian integers. Its prime field was $Z/(3)$, and hence $G/(3)$ was a field of characteristic three. The field $G/(3)$ contained the nine elements.

$$0$$
$$1$$
$$2$$
$$i$$
$$1 + i$$
$$2 + i$$
$$2i$$
$$1 + 2i$$
$$2 + 2i.$$

We see that $9 = 3^2$ and that the dimension of $G/(3)$ considered as a vector space over $Z/(3)$ is two, $(G/(3) : Z/(3)) = 2$. A basis for $G/(3)$ is 1 and i since every element in $G/(3)$ can be expressed in the form

$$a \cdot 1 + b \cdot i$$

where a and b are elements in $Z/(3)$, that is, $a, b = 0, 1$, or 2.

An important notion in the theory of Galois fields is the concept of "roots of unity." Suppose F is a finite field and Π its prime field of characteristic p. Then we may consider the ring of polynomials $\Pi[x]$ over Π, and in particular

$$f(x) = x^n - 1 \in \Pi[x].$$

Now the roots of $f(x) = 0$ lie in some extension field of Π, for example, its splitting field. Note the difference between the point of view of the algebraist and the analyst. In analysis one considers the equation $x^n - 1 = 0$ and endeavors to determine the n (complex) numbers which satisfy this equation identically. In algebra we consider the splitting field of $x^n - 1$ and endeavor to determine the structure of the n (algebraic) elements which satisfy this equation.

If C is the field of complex numbers, then we know that $x^n - 1 \in C[x]$ has n distinct complex numbers as zeros, and furthermore, that these complex numbers form a multiplicative cyclic group. However, we wish to formulate our problem more generally. That is, we ·consider an arbitrary field Δ and the ring of polynomials $\Delta[x]$ over Δ. In this ring we consider the equation

$$f(x) = x^n - 1 = 0.$$

The roots $\omega_1, \omega_2, \cdots, \omega_n$ of $f(x) = 0$ lie in the splitting field of Δ. We shall call these roots $\omega_1, \omega_2, \cdots, \omega_n$ the "n th roots of unity." Of course we cannot prove any results concerning the ω's by resorting to special properties of complex numbers. However, we shall prove many analogous properties, for example, the fact that the ω's form a cyclic group. If we interpret our results in the concrete case of the field C, then the ω's *are* the usual complex roots of unity.

We return then to our prime field Π of characteristic p and consider the equation $x^n - 1 = 0$ in $\Pi[x]$. It will be assumed that p does not divide n, that is, n is not a multiple of the characteristic. The roots $\omega_1, \omega_2, \cdots, \omega_n$ of $x^n - 1 = 0$ which lie in some extension field of Π will be called roots of unity. Our first result is that they are all *distinct*. For suppose $\omega_i = \omega_j$ with $i \neq j$. Then ω_i would be a multiple root of $f(x) = x^n - 1$ and hence a root of the derivative $f'(x)$ of $f(x)$, that is, a root of

$$f'(x) = nx^{n-1}.$$

But from $f'(\omega_i) = n\omega_i^{n-1} = 0$ we conclude that either n or ω_i^{n-1} must be zero since Π is an integral domain. Since by hypothesis $p\nmid n$, we must have $\omega_i = 0$. But this is a contradiction. Hence all the roots of $x^n - 1 = 0$ are simple. The above analysis could also be conducted over a prime field of characteristic zero. Then it is superfluous to add "n is not divisible by the characteristic." Theorems 16 and 17 are also valid for prime fields of characteristic zero.

In the case of the complex number field C, the roots of unity are

$$\omega_r = e^{2\pi i r/n}, \qquad r = 0, 1, \cdots, n - 1$$

and the cyclic group is generated by any ω_r, where r and n are relatively prime, that is, r and n have no common divisors except units. We shall call such a root a *primitive* root of unity. For the general case we have the following definition.

Definition. Let ω be an nth root of unity. If s is the smallest positive integer such that $\omega^s = 1$, we shall say s is the *order* of ω. If the order of ω is n we shall call ω a *primitive n th root of unity.*

Clearly, if ω is any root of unity,

$$\omega^n = 1$$

since ω satisfies the equation $x^n - 1 = 0$. However, there may be integers $s < n$ such that

$$\omega^s = 1.$$

We shall prove that there is at least one root of unity with the property that $n = s$.

If we assume for the moment that ω is a primitive n th root of unity, then the n elements

$$1, \omega, \omega^2, \cdots, \omega^{n-1}$$

are all distinct. (For if $\omega^j = \omega^i$ with $j > i$, then $\omega^{j-i} = 1$, which would imply that the order of ω was less than or equal to $j - i < n$.) Hence we have immediately the following theorem:

Theorem 16. The n n th roots of unity form a cyclic group in which any primitive root is a generator.

This will be used later to prove that the multiplicative group of a finite field is cyclic (cf. Theorem 18). But first we must establish the existence of a primitive root.

Theorem 17. There exists at least one primitive root of unity.

Proof: Let Π be a prime field of characteristic p and let $x^n - 1$ be a polynomial in $\Pi[x]$ such that p does not divide n. The number n is an integer in the ring Z; and since Z is an Euclidean ring without divisors of zero we can decompose n uniquely into prime factors p_k (except for units and the order of the elements),

$$n = \prod_{k=1}^{N} p_k^{n_k}.$$

Among the n roots of unity $\omega_1, \omega_2, \cdots, \omega_n$ there exist at most n/p_i which satisfy the equation $x^{n/p_i} - 1 = 0$, since this equation has at most n/p_i roots. Hence there must exist some ω_i such that

$$\omega_i^{n/p_i} \neq 1.$$

We assert that the order of $\omega_i^{n/p_i^{n_i}}$ is precisely $p_i^{n_i}$. Certainly the order of $\omega_i^{n/p_i^{n_i}}$ is less than or equal to $p_i^{n_i}$ since

$$(\omega_i^{n/p_i^{n_i}})^{p_i^{n_i}} = \omega_i^n = 1.$$

Furthermore, the order must be a divisor of $p_i^{n_i}$, say $p_i^{m_i}$, where $m_i < n_i$. But

$$(\omega_i^{n/p_i^{n_i}})^{p_i^{m_i}} = \omega_i^{n/p_i^{n_i - m_i}} \neq 1$$

by our choice of ω_i. For each i, $i = 1, 2, \cdots, N$ we can find an ω_i with the property that

$$\omega_i^{n/p_i} \neq 1.$$

Consider then the product

$$\omega = \prod_{i=1}^{N} \omega_i^{n/p_i^{n_i}}.$$

We claim that ω is a primitive n th root of unity. For suppose the contrary. Then if ω is of order $m < n$,

$$m = \prod_{k=1}^{N} p_k^{m_k}$$

where $m_k \leqq n_k$ and the equality does not hold in every inequality, $k = 1, 2, \cdots, N$. Suppose for some α, $m_\alpha < n_\alpha$. Then

$$(\omega_\alpha^{n/p_\alpha^{n_\alpha}})^m = (\omega_\alpha^{n/p_\alpha^{n_\alpha - m_\alpha}})^{m/p_\alpha^{m_\alpha}} \neq 1$$

since the p_i are relatively prime.

We have therefore shown abstractly and algebraically that a primitive n th root of unity exists. Our final result in field theory is:

Theorem 18. The multiplicative group of a finite field is cyclic.

Proof: Let F be a finite field containing q elements. By definition of a field, the nonzero elements form an abelian multiplicative group of order $q - 1$. Hence if

$$0, a_1, a_2, \cdots, a_{q-1}$$

are the elements of F, then

$$a_i^{q-1} = 1, \qquad i = 1, 2, \cdots, q - 1.$$

That is, all the nonzero elements of F are roots of the equation

$$x^{q-1} - 1 = 0.$$

The roots of $x^{q-1} - 1 = 0$ are the $q - 1$ roots of unity provided that p does not divide $q - 1$. But $q = p^n$, where n is the dimension of F over its prime field, and hence $p \nmid (q - 1)$. Therefore all the nonzero elements of F are roots of unity. By Theorem 16, they form a cyclic group.

EXERCISES

3.1. A prime field was defined in Section 3.1. Prove that the following definition is equivalent to the one given in the text: "A prime field is a sfield which contains no proper subfields except the null field."

3.2. Prove that the intersection of arbitrary many subfields of a sfield Σ is again a subfield of Σ.

3.3. Prove that a sfield contains one and only one prime field.

3.4. If Z is the ring of integers and N is a prime ideal in Z, prove that there exists a prime number p in Z such that $(p) = N$.

3.5. In the ring of Gaussian integers G, the ideal $(1 - i)$ is prime. What is the characteristic of the field $G/(1 - i)$? What are the elements of this field?

3.6. If p is a prime number in the ring of integers Z, then $Z/(p)$ is a field. Prove that Z has precisely p elements. Is this true for arbitrary finite fields (that is, for fields with a finite number of elements)?

3.7. Prove that (7) is a prime ideal in the ring G of Gaussian integers and construct the field $G/(7)$. [*Hint:* Show that 7 is a prime element in G by the method used in the text, or equivalently, show that the ring of remainder classes $G/(7)$ is free of divisors of zero.]

3.8. How many elements are there in the field $G/(2 + i)$? What is the characteristic of this field?

3.9. If Δ is a field of characteristic p, prove that

$$(a + b)^p = a^p + b^p$$

for all a and b in Δ.

3.10. Prove that the characteristic of a finite field must be a prime number.

3.11. Let K be the field of rational numbers. Let $\phi(x) = x^2 + 1$. Prove that $K[x]/(\phi(x))$ is a field and determine its characteristic.

3.12. Let $\phi(x)$ be any prime element in the ring of polynomials $C[x]$ over the complex field C. Determine the characteristic of $C[x]/(\phi(x))$.

3.13. Let $\varDelta$ be a field contained in a superfield $\varXi$. If θ is an element in $\varDelta$, prove that the simple field extension $\varDelta(\theta)$ is identical with $\varDelta$.

3.14. If $\varDelta$ is a field contained in a superfield $\varXi$, and M is a set in $\varXi$, prove that the intersection of all subfields of $\varXi$ containing both $\varDelta$ and M *is* a field, $\varDelta(M)$.

3.15. Prove that the totality of rational functions in the elements of M with elements of $\varDelta$ as coefficients is a field identical with $\varDelta(M)$. (Cf. the previous exercise.)

3.16. Prove that any finite field adjunction is equivalent to a sequence of simple field adjunctions, that is, prove that if $\varDelta$ is a field, then $\varDelta(\alpha_1, \alpha_2, \cdots, \alpha_n) = \varDelta(\alpha_1)(\alpha_2) \cdots (\alpha_n)$, where $\varDelta$ and $\alpha_1, \alpha_2, \cdots, \alpha_n$ are all contained in some superfield.

3.17. Let K be the field of rational numbers. Show that

$$K(i) \approx K[x]/(x^2 + 1)$$

where $i = \sqrt{-1}$ and K and i are contained in the superfield of complex numbers. By operating with congruences in the ring of remainder classes $K[x]/(x^2 + 1)$, prove that

$$\frac{26}{x^3 + 4x^2 + 2x - 1} \equiv -x - 5 \mod (x^2 + 1).$$

3.18. Let K be the field of rational numbers. Find the defining equation for the field $K(\sqrt[3]{4})$, and discuss this field.

3.19. Let e be the base of natural logarithms and K the field of rational numbers. Is $K(e)$ an algebraic or transcendental extension of K?

3.20. Using the Euclidean algorithm find the "conjugate" of

$$a\xi^2 + b\xi + c$$

where a, b, c are rational numbers and $\xi = \sqrt[3]{2}$.

3.21. Prove that a field contains no proper ideals, that is, if N is an ideal in a field $\varDelta$, then N is either the null ideal or the unit ideal.

3.22. Prove that if $\varDelta$ and $\varXi$ are two fields and $\psi : \varDelta \to \varXi$ is an onto homomorphism, then either $\varXi$ consists of the zero element alone or else the homomorphism is an isomorphism.

3.23. Let $\varDelta$ be a field and x an indeterminate. Show that if α is an element in the field $\varDelta(x)$ but not in $\varDelta$, then α satisfies no polynomial equation over $\varDelta$.

3.24. Let V be the set of all ordered n-tuples of real numbers, $\alpha \in V$ where $\alpha = \{\alpha_1, \alpha_2, \cdots, \alpha_n\}$ and $\alpha_1, \alpha_2, \cdots, \alpha_n$ are real numbers. (Cf. Exercise

1.9.) Let E be the field of real numbers. Define multiplication of an element λ in E by an element α in V by the equation

$$\lambda\alpha = \{\lambda\alpha_1, \lambda\alpha_2, \cdots, \lambda\alpha_n\}.$$

Prove that V is a vector space over E.

3.25. Prove that the set of all real valued functions of the single real variable x which are defined and continuous on the unit interval $[0,1]$ form a vector space V over the real field E when multiplication of elements in V by elements in E is defined in the usual fashion.

3.26. In the vector space V of the previous exercise, determine whether the following sets of vectors are linearly dependent or linearly independent.

   (i) $1, x, x^2$
   (ii) $x, x - x^2, x^2 + 4x, 1 - x^2$
   (iii) $1, \sin x, \cos x$
   (iv) $1, \sin^2 x, \cos^2 x$.

3.27. Show that the two sets of vectors (i) and (ii) of the previous exercise are equivalent sets of vectors.

3.28. From the set of vectors

$$21, x^2, x - 1, x^3 + x^2, -3x + 4, x^2 + 1, x^2 - 3x, 0, x^3 - x, x^3 - 7,$$
$$x^3 + x^2 + x + 1, 3x, 9x^2 - 4x + 8$$

in the vector space of continuous functions of a real variable x over the real field, choose a subset of linearly independent vectors equivalent to this set.

3.29. Show that equivalence of sets of vectors is an equivalence relation. (Cf. Section 2.4.)

3.30. If $f_1, f_2, \cdots, f_n$ and $g_1, g_2, \cdots, g_m$ are two equivalent sets of linearly independent vectors in a vector space V, prove that $n = m$.

3.31. Let V be the vector space of Exercise 1.9 over the real field E. Prove that the set of vectors

$$\{1, 0, \cdots, 0\}$$
$$\{0, 1, \cdots, 0\}$$
$$\cdot \quad \cdot \quad \cdot \quad \cdot$$
$$\{0, 0, \cdots, 1\}$$

form a basis in V and that $n = (V:E)$.

3.32. Show that the vector space of continuous functions over the real field does not have a finite basis.

3.33. If $\varDelta$ is a field and θ is an element algebraic over $\varDelta$, prove that $\varDelta(\theta)$ is a vector space over $\varDelta$. (Both $\varDelta$ and θ are in some superfield $\varXi$.)

3.34. Let $\varDelta_1, \varDelta_2, \varDelta_3$ be fields such that $\varDelta_1 \subseteq \varDelta_2 \subseteq \varDelta_3$. If the rank of $\varDelta_3$ over $\varDelta_1$ is finite, prove that the rank of $\varDelta_2$ over $\varDelta_1$ and the rank of $\varDelta_3$ over $\varDelta_2$ are finite.

3.35. If $\varDelta_1 \subseteq \varDelta_2 \subseteq \cdots \subseteq \varDelta_n$ are fields such that the rank λ_k of $\varDelta_{k+1}$ over $\varDelta_k$ is finite, prove that the rank of $\varDelta_n$ over $\varDelta_1$ is

$$(\varDelta_n : \varDelta_1) = \lambda_1 \lambda_2 \cdots \lambda_{n-1}.$$

3.36. Let $\varXi$ be a superfield containing a field $\varDelta$ and the elements α and β. If α and β are both algebraic over $\varDelta$, prove that $\varDelta(\alpha,\beta)$ is algebraic over $\varDelta$, that is, prove that every element $f(\alpha,\beta) \in \varDelta(\alpha,\beta)$ satisfies a polynomial equation in $\varDelta[x,y]$ with coefficients in $\varDelta$.

3.37. Prove that if $\alpha_1, \alpha_2, \cdots, \alpha_n$ are algebraic over $\varDelta$, then $\varDelta(\alpha_1, \alpha_2, \cdots, \alpha_n)$ is algebraic over $\varDelta$.

3.38. If $\varDelta_1, \varDelta_2, \varDelta_3$ are three fields such that $\varDelta_1 \subseteq \varDelta_2 \subseteq \varDelta_3$, prove that if $\varDelta_3$ is algebraic over $\varDelta_2$ and $\varDelta_2$ is algebraic over $\varDelta_1$, then $\varDelta_3$ is algebraic over $\varDelta_1$.

3.39. Let $\varXi$ be an extension field of the field $\varDelta$. Prove that if

$$(\varXi : \varDelta) = 1$$

then $\varXi = \varDelta$.

3.40. If a field $\varXi$ is algebraic over $\varDelta$, show that $\varXi$ is not necessarily a finite extension of $\varDelta$.

3.41. Define, discuss and show the relation among the following statements.

    (i) $\varXi$ is a simple algebraic extension of $\varDelta$.
   (ii) $\varXi$ is a simple transcendental extension of $\varDelta$.
  (iii) $\varXi$ is a finite extension of $\varDelta$.
  (iv) $\varXi$ is obtained by adjoining a finite number of elements to $\varDelta$.
   (v) $\varXi$ is algebraic over $\varDelta$.
 (vi) θ is algebraic over $\varDelta$.

3.42. Let K be the field of rational numbers. In each of the following cases find an element θ such that $K(\theta)$ is equal to:

    (i) $K(i, \sqrt{2})$.
   (ii) $K(1 + i, \sqrt[3]{4})$.
  (iii) $K(\sqrt[4]{2}, \sqrt[3]{2}, \sqrt{2})$.
  (iv) $K(\sqrt[3]{2}, \omega)$ where ω is a cube root of unity.

What is a defining equation for each field?

3.43. Let $\varDelta$ be a field of characteristic zero and θ an element algebraic over $\varDelta$. Let $f(x)$ be an irreducible polynomial in $\varDelta[x]$ which has θ for a root in $\varDelta(\theta)$. Prove that θ is a simple root.

3.44. Let $\alpha_1, \alpha_2, \cdots, \alpha_n$ be n algebraic elements over the field $\varDelta$ which are separable. Prove that there exists an algebraic element θ such that $\varDelta(\theta) = \varDelta(\alpha_1, \alpha_2, \cdots, \alpha_n)$.

3.45. Let K be the field of rational numbers. Determine the splitting fields of the following polynomials in $K[x]$.

    (i) $x^3 - 1$.
   (ii) $x^4 - 1$.
  (iii) $x^2 + x + 1$.

3.46. Is the field of complex numbers the algebraically closed algebraic extension of the field of rational numbers?

3.47. Prove that if under the isomorphism $\Delta \approx \Delta'$ an arbitrary polynomial $f(x)$ in $\Delta[x]$ is mapped onto $f'(x) \in \Delta'[x]$, then the given isomorphism may be continued into an isomorphism of an arbitrary splitting field $\Delta(\alpha_1, \alpha_2, \cdots, \alpha_n)$ of $f(x)$ over Δ with an arbitrary splitting field $\Delta'(\alpha_1', \alpha_2', \cdots, \alpha_n')$ of $f'(x)$ over Δ', where α_i is mapped onto α_{i_j}', $j = 1, 2, \cdots, n$ and $i = 1, 2, \cdots, n$.

3.48. Let K be the rational field. An element ξ in some superfield is said to be an *algebraic number* if it satisfies a polynomial equation in $K[x]$. Let H be the totality of algebraic numbers. Prove that H is a field which is an algebraically closed algebraic extension of K.

3.49. In Exercises 3.5, 3.7, and 3.8, determine the rank of the given fields considered as vector spaces over their respective prime fields. In each case determine the elements of a basis.

3.50. If $\omega \neq 1$ is an n th root of unity, prove that

$$1 + \omega + \omega^2 + \cdots + \omega^{n-1} = 0.$$

3.51. Let Z be the ring of integers and G the ring of Gaussian integers. Let $\alpha + i\beta$ be a prime element in G. Prove that $G/(\alpha + i\beta)$ is a field of characteristic p, where

(i) $p = \alpha^2 + \beta^2$ if $\alpha \neq 0$, $\beta \neq 0$.
(ii) $p = |\alpha|$ if $\beta = 0$.

Also prove that if q is a prime number in Z, then q is a prime element in G if and only if q is not the sum of two squares in Z.

3.52. Using Theorem 18 prove that Theorem 13 is true even if Δ has only a finite number of elements.

REFERENCES

Albert, A. A., *Modern higher algebra*, University of Chicago Press, 1937.

Beaumont, R. A. and Ball, R. W., *Introduction to modern algebra and matrix theory*, Rinehart and Co., Inc., 1954.

Birkhoff, G. and MacLane, S., *A survey of modern algebra*, rev. ed., The Macmillan Company, 1953.

Jacobson, N., *Lectures in abstract algebra*, Vol. I, D. van Nostrand Co., Inc., 1951.

Jacobson, N., *The theory of rings*, American Mathematical Society, Mathematical Surveys II, 1943.

Johnson, R. E., *First course in abstract algebra*, Prentice-Hall, Inc., 1953.

MacDuffee, C. C., *An introduction to abstract algebra*, John Wiley & Sons, Inc., 1940.

van der Waerden, B. L., *Modern algebra*, Ungar Publishing Co., Vol. I, 1949, Vol. II, 1950.

Zassenhaus, H., *The theory of groups*, Chelsea Publishing Co., 1949.

A P P E N D I X

Sets

A.1 Introduction

In dealing with sets which contain an infinite number of elements there arises a logical question as to whether it is possible to "order" the elements in some prescribed fashion. Such considerations have led mathematicians to postulate the "Axiom of Choice" which we shall consider below. Other forms of this Axiom, generally of a more useful nature in the proof of theorems, are known as "Zorn's lemma" and "Zermelo's theorem." It will be shown in subsequent sections that these three statements are equivalent. Using the Axiom of Choice, we can prove such important results as (cf. Chapter 3), "Every field has an algebraically closed algebraic extension." We shall also indicate other results (cf. Section A.8).

Preliminary even to the statement of the Axiom of Choice we need certain definitions and results found in set theory. While logically we should study sets before exploring groups and rings, the ideas used are conceptually more difficult. We might add parenthetically that we have lost little generality; in fact, the only place where we actually needed Zorn's lemma was in Section 3.4.

In the text proper we used the notion of a set in a rather intuitive fashion and considered the definitions of inclusion, intersection, etc., of two or more sets. A more precise definition of a *set* is to say it is a collection of objects all of which enjoy a certain common property $\mathscr{P}$. That is, given a collection of objects S we can determine whether an element x is in S or is not in S according to whether x has or has not property $\mathscr{P}$. For example, the totality of people in a certain room forms a set. The property $\mathscr{P}$ is that of being in the room. Another example is the collection of all integers Z. One sees that $3 \in Z$ and $\pi \notin Z$ since 3 *is* an integer and π is *not* an integer.

If A and B are two sets, then by $A \cap B$ (read "the *intersection* of A and B") we mean the collection of all elements belonging to both A

and B. (This definition has been introduced earlier in dealing with groups and rings.) By $A \cup B$ (read "the *union* of A and B") we mean the totality of elements belonging to either A or B (or both). We write $A = B$ if A and B contain the same elements and write $A \subseteq B$ if every element of A is in B (equality not excluded). If every element of A is in B but there exist elements in B not in A, then we write $A \subset B$. In this case we say "A is *properly contained* in B." Similarly we define $\supset$ and $\supseteq$. Again, these definitions have been used before. In the cases $A \subseteq B$ or $A \subset B$ we say "A is a *subset* of B." By $B - A$ we mean the totality of elements in B but not in A. The *empty set*, written $\emptyset$, is the set which contains *no* elements. If A and B have no elements in common, then

$$A \cap B = \emptyset.$$

In this case we say A and B are *disjoint*.

A.2 Order Relations

We mentioned earlier the problem of "ordering" elements of a set. A precise definition is indicated.

Definition. Let S be a set and let $\preceq$ be a binary relation defined for elements of S. We say that $\preceq$ is an *order relation* if the following conditions hold:

A1. $x \preceq x$ for every $x \in S$.
A2. $x \preceq y$ and $y \preceq x$ for $x, y \in S$ imply $x = y$.
A3. $x \preceq y$ and $y \preceq z$ for $x, y, z \in S$ imply $x \preceq z$.

The symbol $\preceq$ is not to be interpreted as "less than or equal to" since in general S is not a set of real numbers. If however, S *is* a set of real numbers and $\preceq$ *is* interpreted as "less than or equal to," then we see that less than or equal to *is* an order relation.

If it is possible to define an order relation in a set S, then we say the set is *partially ordered* by the order relation. Further, if a partially ordered set S has the additional property that:

A4. $x \not\preceq y$ with $x, y \in S$ implies $y \preceq x$,

then we say S is *completely ordered by* $\preceq$.

For example, let S consists of the elements

$$S: \quad \{a, b, c, f, k, z, \alpha, \beta, \delta, \epsilon, \xi, \zeta, \lambda, \omega\}$$

where we write $x \preceq y$ ($x, y \in S$) if x does not occur after y in either the Roman or Greek alphabet. This set is partially ordered, but *not* completely ordered. If we define $\preceq$ as above *and* also say that every

Greek letter precedes every Roman letter, then relative to *this* order relation, S becomes completely ordered.

In connection with the above definition of an order relation $\leq$, we find it convenient to define the following symbols:

(a) $x \geq y$ means $y \leq x$.

(b) $x \prec y$ means $x \leq y$ but $x \neq y$.

(c) $x \succ y$ means $y \prec x$.

(d) $x \lesseqgtr y$ means x and y are *comparable*, that is, at least one of the three equations: $x \prec y$, $x = y$, $x \succ y$ is true.

From our definitions of $\leq$, $\geq$, $\prec$, $\succ$, it is clear that if two elements are comparable, then only one of the three relations $x \prec y$, $x = y$, $x \succ y$ can be true.

If a set S is partially ordered, not every two elements of S are necessarily comparable. (Cf. the above example.) If S is completely ordered, then clearly every two elements of S *are* comparable.

Now let S be any set and $\leq$ an order relation defined on S, (that is, S is partially or completely ordered), and let T be any subset of S. Relative to T we make the following definitions.

Definitions. (i) If $t \in T$ has the property that $t \leq x$ for every x in T, then we say t is the *first element* of T.

(ii) If $t \in T$ has the property that there exist no elements x in T such that $x \prec t$, then we say t is a *minimal element* of T.

Clearly every first element is a minimal element, but not conversely. The terms *last element* and *maximal element* are defined in the expected fashion, that is, replace $\prec$ by $\succ$ in the above definitions. If $b \in S$ has the property that $b \leq x$ for all $x \in T$, then we call b a *lower bound* for T. If $g \in S$ is the last element of the set of lower bounds for T, then we call g a *greatest lower bound* (g.l.b.) for T and write $g = $ g.l.b. T. The greatest lower bound is *a* lower bound. Similar definitions hold for *upper bound* and *least upper bound* (l.u.b.).

The following trivial statements will be left as exercises for the reader:

1. First (last) element and greatest lower (least upper) bounds for any T are unique if they exist at all.

2. If T is completely ordered by $\leq$ (whether or not S is), then minimal (maximal) elements are first (last) elements.

3. If T has a first (last) element, then the same element is also the greatest lower (least upper) bound for T.

The converse of 3 is not true. The subset T may have a g.l.b. (l.u.b.) without having any first (last) element. The first, last, minimal, maximal elements of T must belong to T, but upper and lower bounds need not belong to T. For example, let $\preceq$ be "less than or equal to" applied to the set S of real numbers x in the interval $-1 \leqq x \leqq +1$. Let T be the set of real numbers $-1 < x \leqq +1$. Then $-1 \in S$ is the g.l.b. for T, but $-1 \notin T$. Also, T has no first element.

If a set S which is completely ordered relative to $\preceq$ also has the additional property that:

A5. Every nonempty subset of S has a first element, then we say S is *well-ordered* relative to $\preceq$.

An elementary property of well-ordered sets is that "induction proofs" hold in such sets, namely:

Theorem I. Let S be well-ordered under $\preceq$ and let s be its first element. Let T be any subset of S such that: (i) $s \in T$ and (ii) if $x \neq s$ and if $y \in T$ for all $y \prec x$, then $x \in T$. Then $T = S$.

Proof: Suppose $T \neq S$, that is $S - T \neq \emptyset$. We shall obtain a contradiction. Since S is well-ordered, the nonempty subset $S - T$ has a first element, say k. Since $s \in T$, k cannot be equal to s. Now for any $y \prec k$, we have $y \in T$, because k is the *first* element not in T. Then by (ii), $k \in T$, which is a contradiction. Therefore $S - T = \emptyset$ or $S = T$.

A.3 Zermelo's Theorem, the Axiom of Choice, Zorn's Lemma

An important question that arises in abstract set theory is: Which sets can be well-ordered? That is, in what sets is it possible to define an order relation such that the set becomes well-ordered? This leads to an investigation of the axioms of set theory. Zermelo's theorem (ZT) states that every set can be well-ordered and this theorem can be proved, provided we accept the "Axiom of Choice".

To state the Axiom of Choice, we need first the definition of a *choice function*.

Definition. Let S be a nonempty set. Let $\mathfrak{T}$ be the set of all subsets T of S, excluding the empty set. Let ϕ be a mapping of the set of subsets $\mathfrak{T}$ onto S which associates with every subset T of S an element $x = \phi(T)$ of S. Suppose further that $\phi(T) \in T$. Then we shall call ϕ a *choice function* for S.

A choice function is therefore a method of selecting one element from every nonempty subset of a given set S. The Axiom of Choice (AC) states that every set has a choice function.

The third statement, Zorn's lemma (ZL), will be stated in two forms. The first form (ZL1) is "Every partially ordered set S contains a maximal (with respect to set inclusion $\subseteq$) completely ordered subset."

The second form (ZL2) is "If S is a partially ordered set such that every completely ordered subset has an upper bound in S, then S has at least one maximal element."

We shall first show below that the two forms of Zorn's lemma are equivalent. In Sections A.5 and A.6 we shall show the equivalence of the Axiom of Choice, Zermelo's theorem, and Zorn's lemma. These proofs will be preceded by a fundamental lemma (Theorem 3) which facilitates our work. Finally, in Sections A.7 and A.8 we shall give some applications.

Theorem 2. The two forms of Zorn's lemma are equivalent.

Proof: 1. ZL1 implies ZL2.

Assume that the first form of Zorn's lemma holds. Let S be partially ordered by $\preceq$ and suppose that every completely ordered subset of S has an upper bound in S. Let T be a maximal completely ordered subset of S (which exists by ZL1). Then T has an upper bound m in S. Clearly m has the property that $m \succeq t$ for all $t \in T$. We assert that m is an element *in* T. For suppose that $m \notin T$. Then $m \succ t$ for all $t \in T$. Let $\{m\}$ denote the set consisting of the single element m, and let $T' = T \cup \{m\}$. The set T' is a completely ordered subset of S which properly contains T. This contradicts the maximal character of T and hence $m \in T$.

This element m is also a maximal element of S. For if there existed an m' in S such that $m' \succ m$, then $T'' = T \cup \{m'\}$ would be a completely ordered subset of S which properly contains T.

2. ZL2 implies ZL1.

Assume the second form of Zorn's lemma. Let S be partially ordered under the relation $\preceq$. Let $\mathfrak{T}$ be the set of all completely ordered subsets of S. Now $\mathfrak{T}$ is itself partially ordered under the set-inclusion order relation $\subseteq$. Let $\mathfrak{T}_0$ be any completely ordered subset of $\mathfrak{T}$ relative to $\subseteq$, and consider the set $T_0 \subseteq S$,

$$T_0 = \bigcup_{T \in \mathfrak{T}_0} T.$$

We assert that T_0 is completely ordered relative to $\preceq$. For if $x \in T_0$, $y \in T_0$, then $x \in T$ and $y \in T'$ for some T and T' in $\mathfrak{T}_0$. But $\mathfrak{T}_0$ is completely ordered by inclusion. Hence T and T' are comparable and either x and y are in T or in T'.

Suppose for definiteness that x and y are in T'. The set T' is completely ordered relative to $\preceq$ since $T' \in \mathfrak{T}$. Hence x and y are comparable. Therefore T_0 is completely ordered relative to $\preceq$ and $T_0 \in \mathfrak{T}$. Thus every completely ordered subset $\mathfrak{T}_0$ of $\mathfrak{T}$ (relative to $\subseteq$) has an upper bound T_0 in $\mathfrak{T}$. By ZL2, $\mathfrak{T}$ has at least one maximal element relative to $\subseteq$.

A.4 A Fundamental Lemma

The key lemma used in proving the equivalence of AC, ZT, and ZL is Theorem 3, which we state and prove below.

A convenient tool in the proof of the theorem is the notion of an *α-chain* which we proceed to define. Suppose S is a nonempty partially ordered set relative to $\leq$ and suppose that every completely ordered subset of S has a l.u.b. in S. Note that this is a stronger statement than in the hypothesis of ZL2. Suppose further that there exists a function f which maps S into S such that $x \leq f(x)$ for all $x \in S$, and finally, suppose there exist no elements x and y in S such that $x \prec y \prec f(x)$.

Let α be any element of S and hold it fixed. A subset L of S with the properties that:

1. $\alpha \in L$.
2. $x \in L$ implies $f(x) \in L$.
3. If $C \subseteq L$ is a completely ordered subset of S, then l.u.b. $C \in L$

will be called an "α-chain" or simply a *chain* if the element α is understood.

If L_1 and L_2 are α-chains, then so is $L_1 \cap L_2$. Let K be the intersection of all α-chains, $K = \cap L$. Then K is an α-chain, in fact, it is the smallest α-chain; that is, if L is any α-chain, then $K \subseteq L$. We leave the proofs of these statements to the reader.

The element α is the *first* element of K. *Proof*: Let M be the set of all elements x in S such that $\alpha \leq x$. Clearly M is an α-chain. Therefore $K \subseteq M$, and this proves the assertion.

Theorem 3. The set K introduced above is well-ordered with respect to $\leq$ and,

$$f(\text{l.u.b. } K) = \text{l.u.b. } K.$$

Proof: We shall first prove the statement:

(A) If $b \in K$ is comparable with every $x \in K$, then so is $f(b)$.

Let L consist of all elements x in K such that x and $f(b)$ are comparable. We shall show that L is an α-chain. Clearly $L \subseteq K$. The element α must be in L since α is comparable with every element in K (α is the first element of K).

Now we shall prove that $x \in L$ implies $f(x) \in L$. Let x be an arbitrary element in L. Then either

$$f(b) \leq x$$

or

$$x \prec f(b).$$

Now since $x \in K$, we know that $x \preceq f(x)$. Hence if $f(b) \preceq x$, then $f(b) \preceq f(x)$ and thus $f(x) \in L$.

We wish to show even in the case $x \prec f(b)$, that $f(x) \in L$. Since b is comparable with every $x \in K$ and $f(x) \in K$, we know that $b \precsim f(x)$. Hence either $f(x) \preceq b$ or $b \prec f(x)$. [Note that so far we have not used the fact that $x \prec f(b)$.]

Now suppose $b \prec f(x)$. Then either $x \not\prec b$ or $x \prec b$ since b is comparable with every x in K. If $x \prec b$, then

$$x \prec b \prec f(x),$$

which contradicts our assumption about the function f. Thus $x \not\prec b$, that is, either $x = b$ or $x \succ b$.

If $x = b$, then $f(x) = f(b)$ and since $f(b) \in L$, we must have $f(x) \in L$. If $x \succ b$ we have $b \prec x \prec f(b)$, which is the same contradiction as above regarding f. [Note that here is the first time we have used the fact that $x \prec f(b)$.]

In the last two paragraphs we have shown that the statement $b \prec f(x)$ leads to the statement that $f(x)$ is in L. We have left but to consider the case $f(x) \preceq b$. This is simple, since we have $b \preceq f(b)$ and therefore $f(x) \preceq f(b)$. Since $f(x)$ and $f(b)$ are comparable, $f(x)$ is in L.

Hence we see that if $x \in L$, then $f(x) \in L$. We have therefore proved the first two requirements that L be an α-chain. To prove the third, let $C \subseteq L$ be any completely ordered subset of L and let

$$\lambda = \text{l.u.b. } C.$$

Now if there exists an x in C such that $x \succeq f(b)$, then we must have $\lambda \succeq f(b)$, since λ is an upper bound. But if every x in C has the property that $x \prec f(b)$, then $\lambda \preceq f(b)$ since $f(b)$ is a bound. Since λ is comparable with $f(b)$ in either case, we have $\lambda \in L$.

This completes our proof of the statement that L is an α-chain. Thus $K \subseteq L$. But $L \subseteq K$ by definition. Hence $L = K$, which proves the statement (A).

We shall next show that:

(B) K is completely ordered.

Let M be the set of all elements in K which are comparable with every element of K. In particular $\alpha \in M$.

If $b \in M$, then $f(b) \in M$ by statement (A) above.

Let $C \subseteq M$ be a completely ordered subset of M and let $\lambda = \text{l.u.b. } C$. Now if $y \in C$, then y is comparable with every x in K, since $y \in M$. Consider any fixed x in K. If there exists a y in C such that $x \preceq y$, then, of course, $x \preceq \lambda$. If not, then $y \preceq x$ for all $y \in C$ and x is an upper bound for C. Then $\lambda \preceq x$. In either case $\lambda \in M$. Thus we have shown that M is an α-chain. Hence $K \subseteq M$. But $M \subseteq K$ by construction. Therefore $K = M$ and statement (B) is proved.

Finally we shall show:

(C) K is well-ordered.

Let $N \subseteq K$ be any nonempty subset of K. If $\alpha \in N$, then α is the first element of N and our statement (C) is true. Suppose $\alpha \notin N$. Let Q be the set of all elements x in K such that $x \preceq u$ for all $u \in N$. Clearly $\alpha \in Q$.

Let P be any subset of Q. Then P is completely ordered. Let $p = $ l.u.b. P. We shall show that $p \in Q$. For suppose $p \notin Q$. Then there exists a u in N such that $p \succ u$. But every u in N is an upper bound for Q. So

$$\text{l.u.b. } Q \preceq u \prec p.$$

But $P \subseteq Q$. Hence l.u.b. $P \preceq$ l.u.b. $Q \prec p$ or l.u.b. $P \prec p$, which is a contradiction. Therefore $p \in Q$.

Thus the set Q satisfies conditions 1 and 3 for α-chains. If condition 2 is true, then Q is an α-chain. Suppose for the moment that this is true. Then $Q = K$ and $x \preceq u$ for every $x \in K$ and $u \in N$. Thus N has only one element, namely, the least upper bound of K, and therefore N has a first element.

Suppose now that Q is *not* an α-chain. Then there must be an x in Q such that $f(x) \notin Q$. (This is the only possibility since conditions 1 and 3 of an α-chain are true.) Let

$$q = \text{l.u.b. } Q.$$

If x is not equal to q, we assert that $f(x) \in Q$. For if $f(x) \notin Q$, then there would exist a u in N such that $u \prec f(x)$. But $x \in Q$. Hence $x \preceq u$. Equality may be rejected since $x = u$ implies $x \in N$, and since $x \in Q$ we infer $x = q$. Hence $x \prec u \prec f(x)$ which is again a contradiction.

We have now $q \in Q$ and $f(q) \notin Q$. Since $q \in Q$, we must have $q \preceq u$ for all $u \in N$ and since $f(q) \notin Q$, we must have $f(q) \succ u$ for some $u \in N$. Now if $q \notin N$, then $q \prec u$ for every u in N. Then

$$q \prec u \prec f(q)$$

for some u in N. This is a contradiction. Hence $q \in N$ and q is the first element of N.

Thus K is well-ordered and we have proved proposition (C). This also proves the first part of Theorem 3. It remains to show that $f(\text{l.u.b. } K) = $ l.u.b. K. Let $k = $ l.u.b. K. Since K is an α-chain, and, moreover, completely ordered, we know that $k \in K$. (Conditions 1 and 3 of an α-chain.) Furthermore, $f(k) \in K$ by condition 2 of an α-chain and $k \preceq f(k)$ by definition of the f function. Hence $k = f(k)$, which completes the proof of the theorem.

A.5 Equivalence of the Axiom of Choice and Zermelo's Theorem

We shall establish the equivalence of the Axiom of Choice:

Axiom of Choice. Every set has a choice function

and Zermelo's theorem:

Zermelo's theorem. Every set can be well-ordered.

Theorem 4 will show that AC implies ZT, and Theorem 5 will prove the converse.

Theorem 4. The Axiom of Choice implies that every set can be well-ordered.

Proof: Let S be any set and let ϕ be a choice function for S. Let $\mathfrak{X}$ be the set of all subsets of S. This set $\mathfrak{X}$ is partially ordered by set inclusion $\subseteq$. Define a mapping f of $\mathfrak{X}$ into $\mathfrak{X}$ by the equations

(i) $T \rightarrow f(T) = T \cup \{\phi(S - T)\}$ if $T \subset S$
(ii) $S \rightarrow f(S) = S$.

Now $T \subseteq f(T)$ for every $T \subseteq S$, and the existence of a set T' with the property $T \subset T' \subset f(T)$ is impossible, since $f(T)$ contains only one element more than T if $T \subset S$; and no additional elements if $T = S$.

Also let $\mathfrak{A} \subseteq \mathfrak{X}$ be any completely ordered (relative to $\subseteq$) subset of $\mathfrak{X}$ and let

$$U = \bigcup_{A \in \mathfrak{A}} A.$$

Then $U = $ l.u.b. $\mathfrak{A} \in \mathfrak{X}$.

We see that we have fulfilled all the conditions of the preceding theorem with

$\mathfrak{X}$ playing the role of S
$\subseteq$ playing the role of $\preceq$
f playing the role of f
$\emptyset$ playing the role of α.

Let $\mathfrak{K}$ be the intersection of all $\emptyset$-chains. Then $\mathfrak{K}$ is well-ordered relative to set inclusion $\subseteq$.

Define a mapping g of $\mathfrak{K} - \{S\}$ into S by the equation

$$T \rightarrow g(T) = \phi(S - T), \qquad T \subset S.$$

We wish to show that the mapping is one to one, that is, we wish to show that if $T_1 \neq T_2$, then $g(T_1) \neq g(T_2)$.

Suppose T_1 and T_2 are elements of $\Re - \{S\}$ and $T_1 \neq T_2$. Since $\Re$ is completely ordered, T_1 and T_2 are comparable. For definiteness let us suppose $T_1 \subset T_2$; then $g(T_1) = \phi(S - T_1) \in f(T_1)$. Now $f(T_1)$ and T_2 are comparable since both are elements of $\Re$ which is a Ø-chain, and hence completely ordered. If $T_2 \subset f(T_1)$, then $T_1 \subset T_2 \subset f(T_1)$ which contradicts the character of f. Therefore $f(T_1) \subseteq T_2$. Thus $g(T_1) \in T_2$. But $g(T_2) \notin T_2$ since $g(T_2) = \phi(S - T_2) \notin T_2$. Thus $g(T_1) \neq g(T_2)$ and g is a one to one mapping.

We now wish to show that the mapping is *onto*, that is, for every $b \in S$ there corresponds a set V in $\Re - \{S\}$. Toward this end, let b be any element in S. Consider the subsets T of S such that $T \in \Re$ and $b \notin T$, and let V be their union,

$$V = \bigcup_{b \notin T \in \Re} T.$$

(For example, the empty set is one such T.)

As in previous arguments, V is the least upper bound for all such T. Thus $V \in \Re$. But $b \notin V$. However, $b \in S$. Thus $V \neq S$ and therefore $b \notin V \in (\Re - \{S\})$.

Now consider

$$g(V) = \phi(S - V)$$
$$f(V) = V \cup \{\phi(S - V)\}.$$

Since $V \in \Re$ we know that $f(V) \in \Re$ since $\Re$ is a Ø-chain. But $V \subset f(V)$ by definition of the f function. Thus $b \in f(V)$, since otherwise $f(V)$ would be one of the T's such that $b \notin T \in \Re$. But V was an upper bound for the T's. A contradiction.

Then since $b \notin V$ and $b \in f(V)$ we must have

$$b = \phi(S - V),$$

that is,

$$b = g(V),$$

and the mapping g is *onto*.

Now $\Re - \{S\}$ is well-ordered, and this well-ordering is transferred to S by the one to one mapping g. Hence S can be well-ordered, and the proof of the theorem is complete.

The converse is trivial.

Theorem 5. If a set S is well-ordered, then it has a choice function.

Proof: If $T \subseteq S$ is a nonempty subset of S, then T has a first element t since S is well-ordered. Let $\psi(T) = t$. Then ψ is a choice function.

A.6 Equivalence of the Axiom of Choice and Zorn's Lemma

We shall establish the equivalence of the Axiom of Choice:

Axiom of Choice. Every set has a choice function

and Zorn's lemma in its first form:

Zorn's lemma. Every partially ordered set contains a maximal completely ordered (relative to set inclusion $\subseteq$) subset.

Theorem 6 will show that AC implies ZL1, and Theorem 7 will be the converse.

Theorem 6. The Axiom of Choice implies Zorn's lemma (ZL1).

Proof: Let S be a set partially ordered with respect to $\preceq$ and let ϕ be a choice function for S. Consider $\mathfrak{T}$, the set of all completely ordered subsets of S. For each $T \in \mathfrak{T}$, let M_T be the set of all elements x in S such that $T \cup \{x\}$ is still a completely ordered set.

We shall show that for at least one $T \subseteq S$, the set M_T is the empty set. Let f be a mapping of $\mathfrak{T}$ into $\mathfrak{T}$ defined by the equations

$$f(T) = T \cup \{\phi(M_T)\} \qquad \text{if} \qquad M_T \neq \emptyset$$
$$f(T) = T \qquad \text{if} \qquad M_T = \emptyset.$$

Again we have fulfilled the conditions of Theorem 3 with $\mathfrak{T}$ playing the rôle of S relative to $\subseteq$. The mapping f has the properties of the f function of Theorem 3, and any $T \in \mathfrak{T}$ will serve for α. Now from the second part of Theorem 3 we know there exists an element T^* in $\mathfrak{T}$ such that

$$f(T^*) = T^*.$$

For this element T^* we have $M_{T^*} = \emptyset$, so that T^* is a maximal completely ordered subset of S.

The converse is slightly more difficult.

Theorem 7. Zorn's lemma (ZL1) implies the Axiom of Choice.

Proof: Let S be a nonempty set. Now in certain subsets T of S choice functions *can* be defined, for example, the finite subsets. Consider the set $\mathfrak{S}$ of all pairs (T, ϕ) where T is a subset of S and ϕ is a choice function for T.

We define the following order relation for $\mathfrak{S}$:

$$(T, \phi) \preceq (U, \psi)$$

is to mean: $T \subseteq U$, and for every subset $X \subseteq U$ such that $T \cap X \neq \emptyset$

we have $\psi(X) = \phi(T \cap X)$. We may easily verify that $\preceq$ *is* an order relation. Thus $\mathfrak{S}$ is a partially ordered set. Now, by ZL1, let $\mathfrak{T}$ be a maximal completely ordered (relative to $\preceq$) subset of $\mathfrak{S}$.

Consider

$$T^* = \bigcup_{(T,\phi) \in \mathfrak{T}} T,$$

and let (T_1,ϕ_1) and (T_2,ϕ_2) be any two elements of $\mathfrak{T}$. The elements (T_1,ϕ_1) and (T_2,ϕ_2) are comparable, since $\mathfrak{T}$ is completely ordered. For definiteness, let $(T_1,\phi_1) \preceq (T_2,\phi_2)$. Now consider any $X \subseteq T^*$. If $T_1 \cap X \neq \emptyset$, then $T_2 \cap X \neq \emptyset$ and

$$\phi_2(T_2 \cap X) = \phi_1(T_1 \cap (T_2 \cap X)) = \phi_1(T_1 \cap X).$$

In view of the above equations we lay down the following definition: Let X be any nonempty subset of T^*. Choose any $(T,\phi) \in \mathfrak{T}$ such that $T \cap X \neq \emptyset$. Clearly such T's exist. Then define ϕ^* by

$$\phi^*(X) = \phi(T \cap X).$$

The function ϕ^* is a choice function for T^*. Our previous remarks, namely, $\phi_2(T_2 \cap X) = \phi_1(T_1 \cap X)$ show that $\phi^*(X)$ is independent of the choice of T.

Therefore $(T^*,\phi^*) \in \mathfrak{S}$. Furthermore, $(T,\phi) \preceq (T^*,\phi^*)$ for all $(T,\phi) \in \mathfrak{T}$. Hence $T \cup \{(T^*,\phi^*)\}$ is also completely ordered. Since $\mathfrak{T}$ is maximal, (T^*,ϕ^*) must belong to $\mathfrak{T}$ and (T^*,ϕ^*) must be the unique maximal element of $\mathfrak{T}$.

We now assert that $T^* = S$. This will complete the proof of the theorem since T^* has been shown to have a choice function.

Suppose $T^* \neq S$ and let α be an element in S but not in T^*, that is, $\alpha \in (S - T^*)$. Consider the set

$$T_\alpha = T^* \cup \{\alpha\}.$$

Define a choice function ϕ_α for T_α as follows: For every nonempty subset X of T_α let

$$\phi_\alpha(X) = \phi^*(T^* \cap X) \qquad \text{if} \qquad X \neq \{\alpha\}$$
$$\phi_\alpha(X) = \alpha \qquad \text{if} \qquad X = \{\alpha\}.$$

This is clearly a choice function for T_α. But

$$(T^*,\phi^*) \prec (T_\alpha,\phi_\alpha)$$

since $T^* \prec T_\alpha$. Thus $\mathfrak{T} \cup \{(T_\alpha,\phi_\alpha)\}$ would also be completely ordered, which contradicts the maximal character of $\mathfrak{T}$. Thus $T^* = S$.

A.7. Closure of Algebraic Fields

As an application of Zorn's lemma we prove the important theorem:

Theorem 8. Every field Δ has an algebraically closed algebraic extension $\bar{\Delta}$, which is unique up to isomorphisms over Δ.

Proof: Let Φ be the set of all polynomials in $\Delta[x]$ of positive degree with leading coefficient 1. For every $f(x) \in \Phi$ let n_f be the degree of f. Consider the n_f indeterminates $y_{f,1}, y_{f,2}, \cdots, y_{f,n_f}$ and let Y be the set:

$$Y = \{y_{f,1}, y_{f,2}, \cdots, y_{f,n_f}\}_{f \in \Phi} .$$

Adjoin Y (ring adjunction) to the field $\Delta(x)$, viz.: $\Delta(x)[Y]$. We easily see that the ring $\Delta(x)[Y]$ is an integral domain. Let N be the ideal generated by the ring elements

$$\{f(x) - (x - y_{f,1}) \cdots (x - y_{f,n_f})\}_{f \in \Phi} ,$$

that is,

$$N = (\{f(x) - (x - y_{f,1}) \cdots (x - y_{f,n_f})\}_{f \in \Phi}).$$

We shall show that N is properly contained in $\Delta(x)[Y]$. For suppose $1 \in N$. Then

$$1 = \sum_{i=1}^{m} g_i[f_i(x) - (x - y_{f_i,1}) \cdots (x - y_{f_i,n_{f_i}})]$$

identically in the indeterminates where the g_i are elements in $\Delta(x)[Y]$ and m is a finite positive integer.

Let Ξ be the splitting field of the polynomial $f_1(x)f_2(x) \cdots f_m(x)$ in $\Delta[x]$. Ξ is an extension field of Δ. In Ξ replace the y's by their roots. Then $1 = \Sigma g_i \cdot 0 = 0$ which implies $1 = 0$, a contradiction. Hence $1 \notin N$ and $N \subset \Delta(x)[Y]$. Therefore $N \subseteq M$ where M is a maximal ideal in $\Delta(x)[Y]$, (cf. Theorem 9). Consider the ring of remainder classes $\Delta(x)[Y]/M$. By Theorem 13 of Chapter 2, $\Delta(x)[Y]/M$ is a field. Call it Δ^*. By Theorem 11 of Chapter 2 there exists a natural homomorphism ν mapping Δ onto Δ^*. Let $y_{f,j} \to y_{f,j}^*$ under this homomorphism. Now Δ^* contains a subfield Δ_1 isomorphic to $\Delta(x)$, $\Delta(x) \approx \Delta_1 \subseteq \Delta^*$, that is, Δ^* is an extension of $\Delta(x)$. Now $f(x) - (x - y_{f,1}) \cdots (x - y_{f,n_f}) \in N$ and therefore an element of M. Hence under the homomorphism ν it is mapped onto the zero element of Δ^*. But it is also mapped onto

$$f(x) - (x - y_{f,1}^*) \cdots (x - y_{f,n_f}^*).$$

The above expression must therefore be zero. Every polynomial in Φ factors completely in Δ^*. The set Y is mapped onto Y^* and the field $\Delta(Y^*)$ is an algebraic extension of Δ with the property that each y^* is algebraic over Δ and $\Delta(Y^*)$ is algebraically closed.

To prove uniqueness, let $\bar{\Delta}$ and $\bar{\Omega}$ be two algebraically closed algebraic extension of Δ. We wish to show that there exists a mapping ψ which is an onto isomorphism, $\bar{\Delta} \approx \bar{\Omega}$ and such that $\psi(a) = a$ for all a in Δ.

Consider the set $\mathfrak{S}$ of triplets $(\Delta_1, \Omega_1, \phi_1)$ where $\Delta \subseteq \Delta_1 \subseteq \bar{\Delta}$; $\Delta \subseteq \Omega_1 \subseteq \bar{\Omega}$; ϕ_1 is an onto isomorphism of $\Delta_1 \approx \Omega_1$ and $\phi_1(a) = a$ for all $a \in \Delta$. Such triplets exist, for example, (Δ, Δ, ι), where ι is the identity mapping is such a triplet. We define an order relation $\preceq$,

$$(\Delta_1, \Omega_1, \phi_1) \preceq (\Delta_2, \Omega_2, \phi_2),$$

to mean $\Delta_1 \subseteq \Delta_2$; $\Omega_1 \subseteq \Omega_2$; $\phi_1(a) = \phi_2(a)$ for all $a \in \Delta$. By Zorn's lemma there exists a maximal completely ordered subset $\mathfrak{T}$ of $\mathfrak{S}$. Let

$$\Delta^* = \bigcup_{(\Delta_1, \Omega_1, \phi_1) \in \mathfrak{T}} \Delta_1, \qquad \Omega^* = \bigcup_{(\Delta_1, \Omega_1, \phi_1) \in \mathfrak{T}} \Omega_1$$

where $\phi^*(a) = \phi_1(a)$ for some $(\Delta_1, \Omega_1, \phi_1) \in \mathfrak{T}$. The mapping ϕ^* is an onto isomorphism : $\Delta^* \approx \Omega^*$ and $(\Delta^*, \Omega^*, \phi^*) = $ l.u.b. $\mathfrak{T}$.

We shall show that $\Delta^* = \bar{\Delta}$ and $\Omega^* = \bar{\Omega}$. Suppose $\Delta^* \subset \bar{\Delta}$. Then there would exist an $\alpha \in \bar{\Delta}$ such that $\alpha \notin \Delta^*$. The element α is algebraic over Δ and therefore algebraic over Δ^*. Consider the field $\Delta^*(\alpha)$ which is an algebraic extension of Δ^*. By Theorem 14 of Chapter 3, we can extend the isomorphism

$$\phi^*: \quad \Delta^* \approx \Omega^*$$

to

$$\phi^{**}: \quad \Delta^*(\alpha) \approx \Omega^*(\beta)$$

where $\phi^{**}(\alpha) = \beta$. {Note that $\Delta^*(\alpha) \approx \Delta^*[x]/(f(x)) \approx \Omega^*[x]/(g(x)) \approx \Omega^*(\beta)$, where $f(x)$ is the defining polynomial for α and $g(x)$ the defining polynomial for β.} Therefore $(\Delta^*(\alpha), \Omega^*(\beta), \phi^{**}) \succ (\Delta^*, \Omega^*, \phi^*)$. But $\mathfrak{T}$ is maximal, hence this is a contradiction and no such α exists. Therefore $\Delta^* = \bar{\Delta}$. Now $\bar{\Delta} = \Delta^* \approx \Omega^* \subseteq \bar{\Omega}$. The field Ω^* is algebraically closed. Hence $a \in \bar{\Omega}$ implies $a \in \Omega^*$. Thus $\Omega^* = \bar{\Omega}$.

A.8 Further Applications of Zorn's Lemma

In order to demonstrate further the usefulness of our set theoretic axioms we shall prove two additional theorems of ring theory which make use of Zorn's lemma.

Theorem 9. Let R be a ring with a unity element. Then every ideal properly contained in R is contained in a maximal ideal.

Proof: Let N be an ideal properly contained in R and let $\mathfrak{J}$ be the set of all ideals containing N and unequal to R. The set $\mathfrak{J}$ is partially ordered by set inclusion, and by Zorn's lemma contains a maximal completely ordered subset $\mathfrak{M}$. Let

$$M^* = \bigcup_{M \,\in\, \mathfrak{M}} M.$$

Clearly M^* is an ideal, since $\mathfrak{M}$ is completely ordered by set inclusion. (Note that $\bigcup_{M \,\in\, \mathfrak{J}}$ is not necessarily an ideal.)

We assert that M^* is a maximal ideal. First, $M^* \neq R$. For suppose the unity element 1 were in M^*. Then it would be in some $M \in \mathfrak{M}$. But if $1 \in M$, the ideal M would be the whole ring R, a contradiction. Secondly, we assert there exists no ideal M^{**} such that $M^* \subset M^{**} \subset R$. For suppose such an ideal M^{**} existed. Then the set of ideals $\{\mathfrak{M}, M^{**}\}$ would be completely ordered—which contradicts the fact that $\mathfrak{M}$ is maximal.

The second theorem we wish to prove that utilizes Zorn's lemma is the following:

Theorem 10. If R is a commutative ring with a unity element, then every radical ideal N in R is the intersection of a set of prime ideals.

Proof: If $N = R$, the theorem is trivial. If $N \neq R$ there exists an $a \in R$ such that $a \notin N$. Let A be the set of elements

$$A = \{1, a, a^2, a^3, \cdots\}.$$

Then $A \cap N = \emptyset$. Let $\mathfrak{J}$ be the set of all ideals containing N which do not intersect A. By Zorn's lemma there exists a maximal completely ordered subset $\mathfrak{M}$ of $\mathfrak{J}$. Let

$$M_a = \bigcup_{M \,\in\, \mathfrak{M}} M.$$

The ideal M_a has the property that $M_a \cap A = \emptyset$. (For if a^n were in M_a for some integer n, then this would imply $a^n \in M \in \mathfrak{M} \subseteq \mathfrak{J}$, which is a contradiction.)

We wish to show that M_a is a prime ideal. Suppose $b \notin M_a$. Then if (M_a, b) is the ideal generated by M_a and b,

$$M_a \subset (M_a, b).$$

Similarly, if $c \notin M_a$, the ideal M_a is properly contained in (M_a, c),

$$M_a \subset (M_a, c).$$

The ideals (M_a,b) and (M_a,c) also have the property that their intersection with A is not empty, that is,

$$(M_a,b) \cap A \neq \emptyset, \qquad (M_a,c) \cap A \neq \emptyset.$$

Thus there exist nonnegative integers p and n such that

$$a^p \in (M_a,b) \quad \text{and} \quad a^n \in (M_a,c).$$

Hence

$$a^p = r_1 b + m_1, \qquad a^n = r_2 c + m_2$$

where r_1, $r_2 \in R$ and m_1, $m_2 \in M_a$. From the above equations we conclude that

$$a^{p+n} = r_1 r_2 bc + m'$$

where m' is an element in M_a. Thus

$$bc \notin M_a,$$

for if bc were an element of M_a, then a^{p+n} would be an element of M_a. But this is impossible since $M_a \cap A = \emptyset$. We have thus shown that M_a is prime.

The ideal N is contained in M_a. Thus for every $a \notin N$, there exists a prime ideal M_a such that $N \subseteq M_a$ and $a \notin M_a$. Let P be the ideal

$$P = \bigcap_{a \in R - N} M_a.$$

Then $N \subseteq P$. We assert that $N = P$. For suppose $b \in P$ and $b \notin N$. There exists an M_b with $b \notin M_b$. Thus $b \notin P$, a contradiction. Therefore

$$N = P$$

and P is the intersection of a set of prime ideals.

Index